MOLESWORTH RITES AGAIN

I glance around the gathering with the non-chalant insouciance of a man of the world, and suddenly am impaled by a beady eye.

AAARGH!!! It is my former arch-enemy – the Headmaster, Grimes.

And what is that hideous, unfamiliar thing hovering about his features? It is a SMILE – and, even worse, it appears to be intended for me. I try to squirm away into the balding throng, but I am cornered, transfixed by the lethal beam of his geniality. The expression is unnervingly like that of my Head of Department, Grint.

'So, Molesworth . . . how are things?'

'Well, um . . . er . . . erg . . .' Words are as fishbones in my throat.

'And where are you living now, eh?'

'Um . . . er . . . Wimbledon. SIR.' The fatal word slips out unbidden.

'Wimbledon – delightful,' he lies. 'And where are you working?' (Shows how out of date he is – modern headmasters are more tactful and miss out the 'where' from that question.)

'I'm with GBH. SIR.' Again.

'GBH?' he sounds impressed. Everybody has heard of Grabber Bulk Holdings. 'Bet you do all right for yourself with them, eh?'

'Oh, well . . . er . . .'

'No, I'm sure your very successful. Making a few bob, eh, Molesworth?'

This flattery weakens me. 'Oh,' I say casually, lying through my teeth, 'I do all right.'

'In that case,' Grimes leans close and hisses, his ghastly grin inches from my face (gosh he does look like Grint), 'lend us a fiver.'

Nothin

Molesworth is a character created by Geoffrey Willans
and the original drawings were by Ronald Searle.

MOLESWORTH RITES AGAIN

Simon Brett

Illustrations by William Rushton

ARROW BOOKS

To the memory of Geoffrey Willans,
without whom . . . ect.

Arrow Books Limited
17-21 Conway Street, London W1P 6JD

An imprint of the Hutchinson Publishing Group

London Melbourne Sydney Auckland
Johannesburg and agencies throughout
the world

First published by Hutchinson 1983
Arrow edition 1984

© Simon Brett 1983
Illustrations © Hutchinson Publishing Group 1983

Made and printed in Great Britain by the
Guernsey Press Co. Ltd., Guernsey, Channel Islands.

ISBN 0 09 936360 7

CONTENTS

1

I HAVE BEEN HERE BEFORE

'SCOBS,' it says at the top of the card.

I recoil, suspecting vulgar abuse from an office junior, until memory, like a grumbling appendix, reminds me that these letters stand for 'St Custards Old Boys Society'. I lean over the breakfast table, putting my elbow into a pool of mandarin yoguort, and read on.

'NIGEL MOLESWORTH,' it says in blue felt-pen, 'is invited' (this bit in classy black print) 'to the St Custards Old Boys Reunion Dinner.' Dates, times, places follow. I recoil again, aghast.

'What is it?' asks Louise, my spouse and helpmeat. (Yes, gentle reader, it is true. Be not shocked. I know I used to say all those things against GURLS, but I am not the first strong man so to wilt. Sampson succumbed to Delila, Anthony to Cleopatra, and I – even I, Nigel Molesworth – married Louise. I have also pepertuated the Molesworth dynasty with two children, Tristram and Lucinda, but of them *more anon*.)

The card drops from my shaking fingers. Louise picks it up and reads it. 'Oh you must go to this Nigel. It sounds lots of FUN.'

'Never,' I cry. 'It is over twenty years since I left that place and at the time I swore I would never return. Never! *Never!* NEVER! NEVER!'

The Great Hall looks just the same, even though St Cs is no longer a school. (The building has undergone many metamorphososes since it went out of business in the sixties. Gambling club, SAS training centre, stud farm, private hotel, white slave depot, conference centre and now – health spa. But none of the owners have been able to remove the apalling stench of blotch, plastisene, cabbage and disinfectent that is so much part of my youth. That is probably why it keeps changing hands.) SCOBS has booked the place for the evening in a fatally inappropriate gesture of nostaglia.

I look around the shambling throng and unwelcome memories, like ill-digested curry, rise in my gorge. The depressing thing is that none of the beaks seem to have changed at all (well, they were already pretty senile and decrepid when we first knew them), but time has been distinctly unkind to my contemporaries. They can only be in their late thirties, but you wouldn't believe it from the Black Museum of bald pates, pot bellies, bulbous noses, thick glasses, false teeth, crutches, ect, ect, ect., on display.

Thank goodness, I think, curling my Dorian Grey lip in a beautiful sneer, that I have kept my looks.

A hand is clapped bonhomeously on my shoulder. "MOLESWORTH! I HARDLY RECOGNISED YOU – YOU LOOK SO OLD!'

AAARGH!!!

I look at the interruptor of my reveree. His wizzened face means nothing.

'Gillibrand,' he says helpfully. 'Ian Gillibrand. Thought I wasn't going to make it. Late sitting at the House.'

My jaw sags. Did my ears decieve me? Or can it be that the unutterable weed Gillibrand is really a Member of Parliment? Who on earth would elect a twit like that? He was even outvoted for Assistant Vice-Vice-Ink-Monitor in 2B at St Cs.

But it is true.

Oh tempera, oh mores. With the reigns of government in such hands as his who can marvel that the ship of state is tottering down the slippery slope to chaos?

'Oh, look, there's Pauncefoot,' he says and buzzes off, having mastered the politician's skill of not staying anywhere long enough to have to answer any questions.

I glance around the gathering with the nonchalent insousiance of a man of the world, and suddenly am impaled by a beady eye.

8

AAARGH!!! It is my former arch-enemy – the Headmaster, Grimes.

And what is that hidious, unfamiliar thing hovering about his features? It is a SMILE – and, even worse, it appears to be intended for me. I try to squirm away into the balding throng, but I am cornered, transfixed by the lethal beam of his genealily. The expression is unnervingly like that of my Head of Department, Grint.

'So, Molesworth . . . how are things?'

'Well, um . . . er . . . erg. . .' Words are as fishbones in my throat.

'And where are you living now, eh?'

'Um . . . er . . . Wimbledon. SIR.' The fatal word slips out unbidden.

'Wimbledon – delightful,' he lies. 'And where are you working?' (Shows how out of date he is – modern headmasters are more tactful and miss out the 'where' from that question.)

'I'm with GBH. SIR.' Again.

'GBH?' He sounds impressed. Everybody has heard of Grabber Bulk Holdings. 'Bet you do all right for yourself with them, eh?'

'Oh, well . . . er . . .' Shall I admit to him that I have only just been promoted to CJ2/B level and other people (like that odious grammer school erk Darryl Pacey) got to that grade ten years younger? No, why worry him with the internal politics of the Invoice Docketting Department?

'I always knew you were destined for great things,' Grimes goes on. 'One of the most promising pupils I ever taught, Molesworth.'

(The old dotard's mind has clearly gone. The gin, ect., has finally done it's evil work.)

'Oh, well . . . er . . .' I repeat, my manly features suffused by a modest blush.

'No I'm sure your very successful. Making a few bob, eh, Molesworth?'

This flattery weakens me. 'Oh,' I say casually, lying through my teeth, 'I do all right.'

'In that case,' Grimes leans close and hisses, his ghastly grin inches from my face (gosh he *does* look like Grint), 'lend us a fiver. It's impossible to manage on a pension these days and now I havent got the welk-stall any more . . .'

Nothing changes.

Other beaks are there too. Rising above the throng like a mushroom cloud I see the vast hairless dome of Sigismund Arbuthnot, the Mad Maths Master. He must be in his nineties now, a gibbering wreck, still drooling about Pythagoras and babbling of quadratic equations. Nothing, in other words, has changed there either.

An unearthly pallor bleaches his parchment-like skin as he grabs my arm and whispers in horror, 'I have heard a rumour about Peason. Tell me – is it true?'

Now I actually know the answer to this, because Peason is still a mate. We often go out for a beer and comment on the general degeneracy of the modern age. But, remembering Peason's level of achievement in Mathematics back at St Cs, I know I must break the news of his profession gently.

'He is an accountant,' I murmur.

But I have not been gentle enough. Sigismund lets out a strangled cry and his great cranium slumps forward. His pacemaker has fused.

I see another face I know. A Greek God in a pin-striped suite. It is of course Grabber, former head boy of St Cs and winner of the Mrs Joyful Prize for Rafia Work, handsome, fine, upstanding, more patrician in appearance with each passing year.

Since we left St Cs (he to go on to Eton, Harrow, Balliol, the House, Kings, the Guards, the Atheneaeum, ect., ect., ect., I to Grunts), I have in fact kept in touch with Grabber (though he hasn't kept in touch with me). You see, the firm I work for, GBH (Grabber Bulk Holdings), is owned, like everything else, by Grabber Holdings, Inc, of which he is managing director. Every Christmas I meet him at Grabber Towers for an official Grabber Holdings function. Every Christmas he hands me half a glass of S. African sherry, asks if I've made any holiday plans, tells me (without waiting for my answer) about his recent month of skiing at St Mortiz, and complains that the clock in his third Porsche is losing one trillionth of a second every millenium.

'Hello, Molesworth,' he says at the St Custards Old Boys

Dinner, handing me half a glass of S. African sherry. 'Made any holidays plans this year?'

Before I can tell him of our dismal prospects at Rustington-on-Sea, he starts reminicsing about his recent six weeks in the Seyshelles, and complaining that the ashtrays in his second executive jet are too small.

I slip away (he does not notice) and look around for a congeneal face. There are none. Molesworth ii, my apalling brother Steve (who is pretty uncongeneal anyway), has managed to find one of the health farm nurses and is investigating the suana in the basement with her. Peason prudently has decided to give the event a miss and is probably at this moment downing his seventh pint in some relaxing hostlery. (FUMES OF JEALOUSY CLOUD MY SENSES.) Maybe, I think, I too can slip away . . . .

But NO – again I am buttonholed.

'NIGEL!' says a voice of agonisingly familiar wetness. 'Isn't this all FUN!!'

Erg. It is Basil Fotherington-Thomas. Time and the cruel cynicism of the REAL WORLD have failed dismally to shrivel the seeds of optimism in this fatuous youth. He doesn't actually still go around saying, 'Hello clouds, hello sky,' but damn nearly. He believes, against the evidence, that all is for the best in the best of all possible worlds and, unfortunatley, his world and mine do ocasionally overlap. (He is now, to my continuing amazement and his continuing profit, a solicitor. He never showed any signs of being that way at St C's.) It must have been those seven years at Charterhouse. What is worse he lives in Wimbledon so I sometimes come across him. (YURRRGH! Was it not Jean-Paul Belmondo who said, 'Hell is other people'?)

'Very Proustean, isn't it, Nigel?' he gushes on.

'Eh?'

'I mean the evocative nature of this particular school envi-ronement, demonstrating once again the greater power of sen-sation over intellectual memory in our quest for the past as characterised by Marcelle Proust in his *A là recherché dû temps perdue*.'

'Um . . . er . . . yes, of course.'

'Oh, the magical associations of this Great Hall! Oh, the –'

Here, mercifully, he is stopped by someone clapping hands for attention.

Ah, I think, here it comes – the plea for money.

But no. In a voice weak with emotion Grimes asks all present to join their voices in the St Custards School Song. Miss Pringle, who has been exumed from some mortuary, sits at the school piano (also exumed specially for the occasion after its premature demise when Molesworth ii played Fairy Bells on it *con* too much *brillo*). She thumps out that never-to-be-forgotten opening PLUNK.

Unwittingly (and in my case unwillingly) our voices join in the familiar words:

> *Pueri Custardienus!*
> *Cotta vincit Labienus.*
> *Ad hoc ex officio*
> *Et stet semper status quo . . .*

While the words are sung, I look around for the traditional smiles of derision. I listen for the conspiratorial sniggers.

THERE ARE NONE. Instead, hairy nostrils quiver, veined noses are brusquely rubbed, and unwishedfor tears gather at the corners of bloodshot eyes. Good grief, they are actually taking it seriously!!!

To my fury, I feel a tickling in my own jaundiced eye, and blow my nose surrepticiously as we sing on:

> *De gustibus non est disputandum,*
> *Sine qua non nil desperandum,*
> *E pluribus unum memorandum,*
> *Et quod erat demonstrandum . . .!*

As I look around me I realise the great TRUTH – viz. The REAL WORLD is not so very different from the hallowed cloisters of acadeem (classy writing, huh?). It is still peopled with oiks, weeds, cissies, wets, bullies, stinkers, sneaks and goodie-goodys. Only now they are all *in theory* (her-her hollow laughter) grown-ups.

'*Plus cà çhange,*' in Votlaire's immortal words, '*plus c'etês le meme çhose.*'

And my skills are still of value. I, Nigel Molesworth – still smiling, still cunning, still sauve and debonair, my cynicism untarnished, a solid groyne resisting the steady wash of time on the beachhead of experience (more classy stuff) – can apply to the Eighties my basic life-principal: How To Get By With The Minimum Effort.

Bearing this in mind, I let the others sing and for myself just mouth the last line of the School Song:

> *Victor ludorum!*
> *Pons Asinorum!*
> *Mea culpa et quo vadis –*
> *Quis custodiet Custardis!*
> *QUIS CUSTODIET CUSTARDIS!!!*

2

WIVES

For 'Sex' see Chapter 11

Social life is pretty hard and it gets harder as you grow increasingly seer and yellow. I mean you spend years learning to adjust to your friends' revolting habits and peculiarities and just when you've got that licked, they MARRY and you have to start the whole process all over again.

Perfectly ordinary men do develop these extrordinary wives. I mean, look at some of the St Cs crowd . . . .

BASIL FOTHERINGTON-THOMAS's wife Araminta is exactly like his sister Arrabella. They were schoolfriends and are both into macramee and wholefood. How he tells them apart beats me.

I sometimes fantesize about their domestic life. (Not smutty fantesies you understand – smuttyness and B.F-T do not go together. I know he and Araminta have produced 2 children, Thoby and Ghislane, but they must have done it in some hygeinic way that didn't involve bodily contact. The imagination cannot cope with the idea of Basil actually . . . as I say, it cannot cope.) No, I refer to fantesies of Araminta and Arrabella (who always seems to be staying there) preparing for the heros return from a hard days soliciting . . . .

(The scene is the kitch. of the Fotherington-Thomas Edw. semi in the leafy purleius of Wimbledon Village. There is a print of Desiderata on the wall: on a strippedpine table Araminta and Arrabella roll out manure-coloured pastry with a strippedpine rollingpin. They sing their old school song as they work.)

ARAMINTA   Ho for bat, Ho for ball

ARRABELLA   Ho for hockey and lax and all
            Miss Dennis is strict,
            Miss Hamilton fair
            But Miss Peabody (Gym) is both strict and tall.

(They collapse into each other's arms, giggling girlishly.)

ARRABELLA   Oh the happy times that we had at St Dulcibellas!

ARAMINTA   Oh indeed! And none happier than the first day I
           met you, Arrabella!

ARRABELLA   *(fondly)* Ah!

ARAMINTA   For if I had not met you I would not have met
           Basil whence springeth all my happiness!

ARRABELLA   *(fondly)* Ah! I hope he will like this leak, nettle and
            cumfrey quishe!

ARAMINTA   I am sure he will for the food prepared with the
           hand of love satisfies not only the hunger of the
           stomach!

ARRABELLA   *(fondly)* Ah! I wish I had said that, Araminta! Oh,
            all is happiness!

ARAMINTA   Indeed! And hark – I hear Basil's key in the lock!

ARRABELLA   Oh joy!

ARAMINTA   Ah bliss!

ARRABELLA   Oh!

ARAMINTA   Ah!

ME (suffering from nausia of the imagination) UGH!

Here mercifully my fantesy ends. It is too grusome and the
more so for probably being true.

GRABBER's wife is called Felicitiah (*neigh* Devereaux-
ffincham-ffitz-william-ffrensch-ssmith-Walsinghame). She is
kept in a bank valt and only brought out on special ocasions.

   She is beautifully GROOMED and spends at least three days
before each special ocasion having her body tuned, her skin
Frenchpolished, her fingernails goldplated, her teeth mani-
cured, her hair massaged, ect., ect., ect.

   Her life contains a lot of special ocasions. Apart from Grabber
Holdings functions, dos at Buck House, Lord Mayors Ban-
quettes, ect., ect., ect., there are also Ascot, Henly, Wimbledon, Glynborne, ect., ect., ect., not to mention about nine

months holiday spent variously in St Mortiz, St Lucia, St Troppez, the Seyshelles, ect., ect., ect. . . .

She does not DO anything. There is a Little Woman who gets her up in the morning, a Little Woman who gets her dressed, a Little Woman who feeds her, and a Little Woman who holds up a hand when she yawns (which she does quite often).

She is the mother of two children (both at Eton and Bennenden), but probably a Little Woman had those for her.

PEASON has married 'beneath him'. I did not realise at first, but Louise, who knows about these things (i.e. is a SNOB), told me.

Timothy Peason's wife is called Sharon and is fifteen years younger than he (grammer). Louise thinks it's disgusting him having a mere child 'ministring to his every need', but I think it has a lot to be said for it. Louise says Sharon treats him like a 'little tin god' and never crosses him and that's not a good idea *is it?* (If only I had known Louise when I did Latin at St Cs; then I would have understood what the beaks ment when they kept going on about QUESTIONS EXPECTING THE ANSWER NO.) Louise says it must be 'demeening for a man' being 'cowtowed to' by such a 'brainless bit of fluff' and I wouldn't like that *would I?* (I am tempted to admit I wouldn't mind trying it, but the words freeze on my lips.)

Anyway basicly Sharon lets Timothy do what he wants – nights out with the boys, watching football, snooker, darts, wrestling ect. on the television whenever he feels like it, getting drunk, picking his nose, never doing washingup, making beds, changing nappies ect. – without demurr. Louise says that's no basis for a marriage, *is it?* (On the other hand eminant physcologists have said that marriage should ideally be a realisation of the partners' individual identity, and Sharon does allow Timothy to realise his full potencial as a SLOB, which is what he always was.)

Sharon is a product of the State Education System and, according to Louise, has some 'very common vowells'. She also dresses in 'rather vulgar clothes' (i.e. blouzes cut down to her waist and skirts cut up to quite near her waist) and she wears a lot of 'flashy jewellery'. Louise suspects that before Sharon got married she was (PAUSE TO THROW HANDS UP IN HORROR) – a BARMAID!!! (This is actually quite likely. Where else would Peason have met a woman?)

Anyway Louise doesnt think Sharon is 'our sort of person'. She thinks the Peasons' relationship is 'distinctly rocky' and feels that the 'difference in their backgrounds' is bound to lead to 'martial problems in the future.'

However there is no sign of these coming. To Louise's amazement (and frustration) THE MARRIAGE SEEMS TO WORK.

I am also amazed but for different reasons. What surprises me is what SHE sees in HIM. I mean Timothy Peason is a nice enough bloke, but he does have the physical charm and allure of a seed potatoe.

I cannot understand it. (Though every time I contemplate it FUMES OF JEALOUSY arise, along with the thought – Why didn't I wait? Why did I take the plunge so tragicly young? Why didn't I hang around until I could impress some lasivious teenager with my sophistication and *savoie-fair*?)

Probably, as is usually the case (so I'm told), the secret of the relationship is SEX. Certainly Peason walks around with a glazed expression and fatuous smile on his face most of the time. (On the other hand he used to look like that when he was at St Cs and I'm sure regular sex wasn't the reason then.)

MY APALLING BROTHER STEVE (a.k.a MOLES-WORTH ii) does not have a wife. In spite of his repellent appearance (his receding perm and his Status Quo satin bomber jacket), he has a STREAM OF WOMEN and is FRANKLY PROMISCUOUS, which I, as a married man, think is pretty disgusting (FUMES OF JEALOUSY).

Some of the people I work with at GBH do have wives.

MY HEAD OF DEPARTMENT, GRINT, has one called Marcia. She has a CAREER OF HER OWN and we are NEVER ALLOWED TO FORGET IT.

She is a high-powered executive in a multinational cosmetics firm (owned ultimately of course by Grabber Holdings, Inc. – in fact one of their most popular fragrences is called 'Grabber No. 5') and is always attending meetings in Rome, New York,

Carraccas, Tokio, ect., ect., ect. She is paid huge sums of money, so between them their annual income is trillions and trillions of pounds which explains the flat in town country estate converted abbey in the Dordonge, ect., ect., ect.

Marcia Grint has produced 2 children (currantly undergoing private education in Switzerland), though since she and Grint are never in the same continent I don't know how.

That odious grammer school erk DARRYL PACEY has a wife called Carole, so one has to introduce them to people as 'Darrylandcarryl'. She is small and neat and dresses demurely. She is the complete company wife, as devoted to GBH as Darryl is.

She thinks Darryl is wonderfull (which says all there is to say about her intelectual qualities) and has never been heard to say anything that was not direct quotation from him. She can talk with great fascility about increments, grading systems and staff numbers, but has never ventured an opinion on anything else.

The only person Carole thinks is more wonderfull than Darryl is (with Darryl's full approval and indeed encouragement) Grint. It is bad enough to hear Darryl constantly sucking up to the Head of Department; to hear Darrylandcarryl at it is totally nausious (sufficient – if anything were needed – to make any GBH social function quite intolerable).

Sometimes I fantesize about Darrylandcarryl in bed. (I know I shouldnt, but I do; its a symtom of gallopping dirtyoldmania).

The scene is Darrylandcarryl's bedroom. Over the bedhead hangs a photograph of Grint. Darryl has just allowed himself 3 minutes 23.39712 seconds off from the GBH work he has brought home for a bit of Sex, because he has just read a new bock on management tecniques which says that it is important for young executives to be sexually fullfilled so that their thoughts do not wander while they are working.

(*who has read in the same book that sex should be* enjoyable) Oh, that was ENJOYABLE.

CARRYL (*who always agrees with Darryl whatever happens*) Yes, it *was* ENJOYABLE.

DARRYL It was almost as good for me as when I was told by Grint in my Annual Interview that I had been given

a Special Merit Award which raised my Grade to
CJ2/B+1(SMA).

CARRYL It was almost as good for me as when I heard that
GBH Pension Sceme Benefits were to be index-
linked for all staff above PGT3 level.

DARRYL (*musing*) When I reach CJ3/A level it will be tax-
efficient for us to have a baby.

CARRYL Oh, how exiting! We would be able to announce the
birth in the GBH House Magazine!

DARRYL Yes, and we could ask Grint to be a godfather! And
when he's old enough our son could join GBH at
HJGL8/d4 Trainee level!

CARRYL (*for whom life could hold nothing more than this prospect*)
Oh, Darryl!!!

DARRYL (*for whom life could hold nothing more than this prospect*)
Oh, Carryl!!!

Once again nausia of the imagination drags me screaming from
fantesy to the REAL WORLD.

Of course there are many other sorts of wives. Being married
to one leads to introductions to others and it is quite useful to
be able to recognise at-at-glance what sort it is and WHAT
ONE IS UP AGAINST.

With a view to helping my gentle reader in this difficult task,
I have devised a chart which categorises the more common
species and gives advise on how to recognise them. The main
function of this is so that once you have identified the species
from it's call you know what else it's going to say and DONT
HAVE TO LISTEN ANY MORE. ('A boon to husbands.
My social life was unutterably dreary – everyone knew me by
my bent ears until I discovered the MOLESWORTH AT-A-
GLANCE WIFE RECOGNITION CHART.' Mr M. J. of
Letchworth.)

THE MOLESWORTH AT-A-GLANCE WIFE RECOGNITION CHART

Species	Distinctive features	Distinctive calls	Mating call*
THE WOOLY LIBERAL	Wears jeans and a Gurnsey sweater; no makeup. Does not shave armpits.	'We won't have a television in the house.' 'All our vegetables and children have been produced naturally.' 'We won't let our children play Happy Families because we feel that it cramps their thinking into the straightjacket of stereotype.'	'I think we should make a further exploration of the physical plain of our relationship.'
THE NESTING EARTHMOTHER	Wears smocks (Laura Ashely numbers with little flowers all over them) whether pregnant or not. Has encrustations of yoguort ect. from babies on shoulders of all garments; and bits of Leggo and half-eaten biscuts in pockets.	'It's impossible to keep the house tidy when youve got children, so I don't try.' [NB – every other sentence contains the words 'when youve got children'.] 'The baby and Julian are both devoted to my breasts.' 'We had just the same trouble with ours.'	'Come on, Julian. You can sqeeze in between me and the baby. But be quiet.'

* These are inevitably conjectueral, but my knowledge of the world convinces me they are correct – Ed.

Species	Distinctive features	Distinctive calls	Mating call
THE TWITTERING WORRIER	Wears glasses and blinks a lot. Wears crimplene and tricel.	'The doctor thinks it may be an allergy.' 'I just wonder what *effect* its having on them.'	'Are you sure it'll be all right?'
THE DOMESTIC GAULEITER	Wears spotless blouzes and skirts, which have been IRONED (v. rare in wives). Shouts a lot. Wraps everything in Clingfilm.	'No child in this house gets a toy out of the toy-cupboard without a requisition!' 'What do you mean – bed? You havn't done the washingup yet!' 'You can come into the front room but dont let me catch you disarranging the books.'	'Tonight, Charles, SEX!''
THE BABY GUSHER	Wears brightly-colored dungerees. Refers to everyone as 'we'. Never raises voice; talks in questions.	'Arent we lovely?' 'Have we done something naughty?' 'Are we going to eat up our dinners?' 'Did we fall on our botty-wotty?'	'Are we going to have sexy-wexy, Nicky-Wicky?'

Species	Distinctive features	Distinctive calls	Mating call
THE HIGH ACHEEVER	Wears expensive clothes which are regularly drycleaned and well-put-on makeup (v. rare in wives). Works out babysitting payments on calculator and asks if babysitters are registerred for VAT. Can do EVERYTHING.	'The children get a lot of feedback from my being away so much.' 'I'm going windserfing after my facial and then meeting James at the National Theatre.' 'Sorry, cant make the coffeemorning – I'm in LA that week.' 'It's simply a matter of organisation.'	'Quick. I've got 2 mins 14 secs before I have to go to Heathrow.'
THE DOUBLE ACT	Wears ernest expression. Transfixes you with eye. Holds husbands hand a lot.	'Gregory and I are very much a UNIT.'' 'Children would only spoil it.' 'Gregory and I have talked this through and are in full agreement.'	'Shall we Gregory or would you rather talk about it for an hour or so first?'

Species	Distinctive features	Distinctive calls	Mating call
THE WHINGEING LIBBER	Wears very thin very quickly. Does not shave armpits or legs. Talks pugnatiously, daring you to think of her as a sex-obj. *	'I'm a PERSON first and a woman second.' 'You're falling straight into stereotype.' 'I'm damn well not going to do it – it's his turn.'	'Oh God, I suppose you want your pound of flesh.'
THE SEXPOT†	Wears diaphonous garments that melt away at my passionate touch.	'Nigel, I have been waiting all my life for a man like you. Let us get out of these mockeries of clothes.' 'Oh Nigel you are so good!' 'Oh Nigel that was so GOOD!'	SEE PREVIOUS COLUMN

* No danger of that from me – Ed.
† This species is very rare. In fact, if my experiense is anything to go by, its exstinct. – Ed.

AND THEN OF COURSE THERES
LOUISE . . .

Yes, well, LOUISE . . .

How did we meet? Was there magic in the air? Was it some enchanted evening? Did I suddenly hear a stranger laughing across a crowded room? Was she just seventeen (if you know what I mean) and did I see her standing there? Did I never hear the birds in the trees until there was Louise? Was I all shook up?

QUITE HONESTLY I CAN'T REMEMBER.

I just know that our meeting marked a great watershead in my life. So much so that my history could almost be divided into BL (Before Louise) and AL (Anno Louisiae). (BL is a period I look back on with increasing nostaglia.)

I remember WHEN and WHERE we met, but I don't remember exactly WHAT HAPPENED.

The venue was bad enough. Even my manly cheek succumbs to a blush to confess that I met my wife at a Young Conservative Hop!

Let me hasten to assure you that this was not my usual style. Politics didn't come into it so far as I was concerned. (I've never really had any politics except a vague general feeling that everything ought to be shared out equally except *my* things.) But Ian Gillibrand (the MP of the SCOBS reunion) had roped me in. There I was, three years out of my public school, Grunts, already in GBH (at CJ1/J Level) and Gillibrand, poor sap, I suppose thought I might yet become a PR executive, local councillor, Mafia hitman, investment consultant, bent solicitor or someone else useful to an aspiring Tory politician. (When, shortly afterwards, he realised I was never going to represent more than one very uncertain vote, he dropped me like the wrong end of an electric butterknife.)

Anyway, so there I was at this Hop. Beatles were in the air . . . (Note restraint – no cheap DDT jokes.) The lights were dim . . . (So were most of the girls, but just my luck I didn't get one of them – I got Louise.) I was resplendent in my DJ with the drainpipe trousers and rolled satin lapel which I'm still waiting to come back into fashion. Louise was in this long pale blue strapless dress held up by some spinoff from the pipe-cleaner industry and . . . and . . . and . . . .

Here recollections get hazey. I remember Ian Gillibrand saying, 'Must introduce you to Louise,' and whispering, 'Convent-educated – they always say they're the worst, eh, ha, ha,' and me thinking (mistakenly) that he meant she was rampantly sexual and lassivious and . . . and . . . and . . . .

Memory (assisted by a particularly vile fruitcup) clouds the rest of the evening.

When I was next aware of time, Louise and I, in the parlance of the time (at least the Young Conservative parlance of the time) were GOING STEADY.

The only comparible experience I can think of is when I had my wisdom teeth out – the same not unpleasant vague loss of consiousness, the same tampering with my sense of time, and the same feeling that I'd been kicked in the face by a horse when I eventually came round.

And in many ways that's how our RELATIONSHIP has continued.

Most couples you hear say how they're longing to GET THE CHILDREN OFF THEIR HANDS and HAVE A BIT OF TIME ON THEIR OWN. (NB – This is always followed within 1 min 30 secs by either the expression 'potter through France' or alternatively *tour gasteronomic*.)

I am not sure about this. While GETTING THE CHILDREN OFF ONES HANDS is a consommation devoutley to be wished for, being alone with Louise for any length of time is A SITUATION FROUGHT WITH RISKS.

You see, when we got married, Louise reckoned she could MAKE SOMETHING OF ME. (I didnt realise this at the time – the ghastly truth trickled out slowly.) She obviously saw herself as some sort of Svengali or Pigmalion – I was the putty in her hands which she would reshape into an IDEAL HUSBAND.

Huh.

She tried, but she hadnt quite reckoned on the resiliance of my putty.

Anyway, one of the GOOD THINGS about having Tristram and Lucinda was that they KEPT LOUISE BUSY and so she had to lay off her major project.

I am just worried that when we do GET THE CHILD-REN OFF OUR HANDS, she will turn the full force of her bulldozers on me again and get under way with the NIGEL MOLESWORTH RECLAMATION AND RE-DEVELOPEMENT SCEME (for which plans may ultimately be viewable at the Town Hall).

Shes never said exactly what she would like me to be, though she has made it VERY CLEAR that she would like me differ-ent. However she has dropped enough hints for me to be able to piece together an outline of what she has in mind.

Basicly I think she wants to convert what she regards as something unsightly and non-functional into a kind of elaberate and sleek ARTS COMPLEX.

If she actually did draw up plans, I bet they'd look something like this . . . .

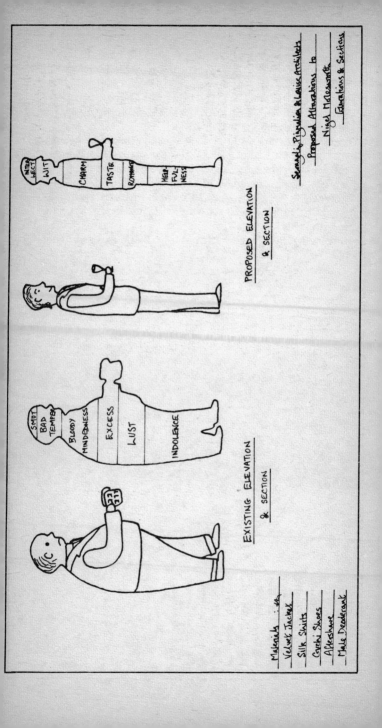

Materials: ie
Velvet Jacket
Silk Shirts
Greeki Shoes
Aftershave
Male Deodorant

EXISTING ELEVATION
& SECTION

SMUT
BAD TEMPER
BLOODY
MINDEDNESS
EXCESS
LUST
INDOLENCE

PROPOSED ELEVATION
& SECTION

INTELLECT
WIT
CHARM
TASTE
ROMANCE
HELP-
FUL-
NESS

Scrooge, Playwise & Lewise Architects
Proposed Alterations to
Nigel Molesworth
Elevations & Sections

Demolish existing brain structure; clean out lumber, remove lassitudes & thoughts of chasleen at the office, 16-yr-old baby-sitter, loaders, ect. Make good. Remove bloodshotness from eyes, flabbiness from cheeks, incipient cones from nose, truculence from mouth. Advance receding hairline. Make good.

HEAD SECTION
(EXISTING)

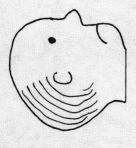

HEAD SECTION
(PROPOSED)

Fill vacant brain cells with thoughts of Frank Lloyd Wright, Fashion, Bangs, Patrick White, ect. Make good. Elevate noble intellectual brow. Arrange mouth into line of aristocratic charm and fill with dazzling bon mots. Arrange tidy haircut.

Scrungali, Piggnahar & Leavine Architects to Proposed Alterations to Nigel Molesworth — Top Story — Detail

3

ENTERTAINING

Or, La Vie D'Elegance in SW20

Louise has PRETENSIONS about entertaining. She keeps on about getting 'the right mix' in our guests and I think she sees herself as the Madam de Stëal of Wimbledon, conducting a literary *saloon* famous for its dazzle and wit.

To this end she keeps inviting what she calls 'artistic' people to dinner. Her theory is that if you assemble Lucinda's piano teacher, two pillars of the amatuer dramatic society and the cinema critic of the local paper, give them enough *garlique* and Chateaux Grabbeaux Algerian Bordeau-style plonk, and leave them to their own devices, the evening will sparkle.

SHE IS WRONG, but no amount of failures stop her from trying it again.

And what, you may ask, is my role in the proceedings? My most sensible course would obviously be to go out for a few pts with Timothy Peason and leave Louise to get on with it.

But this I am not allowed to do. Instead I am expected to stand around pouring out plonk for all these affected twits, coruscating with wit the while and dropping *bon meaux* with the whole miserable shower.

I think I have a rough idea of how Louise thinks such evenings should go – in a kind of shimmer of Wildian repartee as her husband demonstrates the supreme qualities of his MIND (one of the many reasons for which she married him). E.g . . .

IST AFFECTED TWIT	Tell me, Nigel, how would you define Art? *(He gets out his notebook and pencil to note down my replies for the collection of my tabletalk which he is editing for Messrs. Grabber & Grabber.)*
ME *(with casual fluency)*	Art, my dear man, is simply the tension between Reality and the Medium. The greater the tension, the greater the Art. The greatest Art can therefore be said to be the tightest.
AFFECTED TWITS *(tutti)*	Gosh yes. He's right of course, I'd never thought of that, ect.
ME *(quipping condessendingly down to their level)*	And in some cases the greatest Artists have also prooved to be the tightest.
AFFECTED TWITS *(tutti)*	Ha ha ha ha.
2ND AFFECTED TWIT	But, Nigel, what would you say is the place of Art in Society?
ME	Society, as it is generally undestood, combines the maximum irellevance with the minimum individuallity and imagination. Art, *au contrairre*, combines individuallity and imagination to produce rellevance. Art and society are therefore mutually exclusive.
AFFECTED TWITS *(tutti)*	Gosh, Lummy, What on earth's he on about, Too deep for me, ect., ect.
ME	For a man to be an Artist, he must present Truth; for him to be a part of Society, he must limit Truth. The skills of Art are those of revalation; the skills of Society, of concealment. Therefore there can be no dialoge between Art and Society without a critical interpreter . . . ect., ect., ect.

WHEREAS IN FACT what we get at our dinner parties is more like this:

1ST AFFECTED TWIT	I'm working on a new production of *Macbeth* which sees him as a figure whose identity has been so consumed by his wife that he is reduced to a state of Kaffkaesque alienation. How do you respond to that interpretation, Nigel?
ME	Um . . . er . . . well . . . *(a brainwave)* I put up some cieling tiles over the weekend.

(THIS IS NOT ACTUALLY TRUE, but cieling tiles always gets people talking at dinner parties. So does grouting – everyone has their own grouting anicdote. Morgages, house prices and education are also good topics. Art is always a non-starter.)

And once again Louise is left wondering why she actually DID marry me.

SOME INVITATIONS

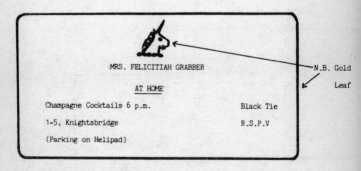

Much to Louise's chagrine, *we are not on the distribution list for one of these. She rather fancies herself in this sort of social* milieue.

> Basil and Araminta invite you to join them to hail the Summer Solstice and celerbrate the opening of their Cowparsly and Privett wine.
>
> [Morris Dancing at 9 pm.] Bring your own Corndolly

If this comes through your letterbox, arrange a prior engagement *IMMEDIATELY*.

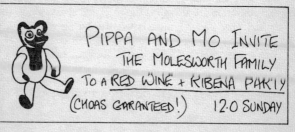

> PIPPA AND MO INVITE THE MOLESWORTH FAMILY TO A RED WINE + RIBENA PARTY (CHOAS GARANTEED!) 12.0 SUNDAY

These can be OK, so long as you get drunk enough quick enough not to notice all the children. Equally they can be apalling.

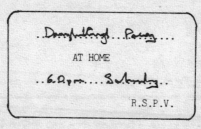

> AT HOME
>
> R.S.P.V.

Well, if you want to hear even more about the GBH Grading System, I suppose you might enjoy this.

Whatever my fantesies, I have to recognise the fact that my apalling brother's scene is NOT MY SCENE.

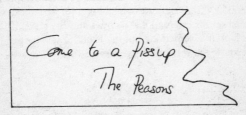

This seems to me the ideal invitation – pithy, informative and welcoming. (Louise does not agree.)

I actually went to this one because Charleen at the office is amazingly dishy and Louise was staying with her mother and I thought well its worth trying you never know your luck. But I decided fancy dress was rather demeening and childish, so wore my own clothes. I won first prize.

35

Louise doesnt only have PRETENSIONS about conversation during dinner parties, but also about what is served up for the guests to eat.

Some years back her mother gave her an annual subscription to *Gastrognome* (pub. monthly by Grabber Magazines, Inc.) and since then I havent seen what I call REAL FOOD.

Now every sausage is smothered in some gunge and even baked beans on toast are transmorgified into *haricos en cocotte garni à la sauce de tomatoes et beacoup de garlique sur le pain tostée.*

The aim of Louise's dinner parties (I'd say *our* dinner parties, but I may as well call a spade a spade) is to produce peculiar dishes from as many different countries as possible. She spends hours raiding the Delicatessen counter of the local Grabbo Supermarket for international dainties and the result is that her menus look like something out of 'Jeaux Sans Frontiers'.

You know the sort of thing I mean . . . .

MENU

1ST COURSE
Mexican Avacado and Pimmento Salad with Chinese
Gooosberry Sauce

2ND COURSE
Japanese Raw Fishballs, with Andelusian Stuffed Courgets,
Cellariac Grattiné Provencalé, Javanese Curried Lentels and
Lithuanian Potatoe Pancakes

3RD COURSE
Zabagallone di Roma
or
Bengali Tingabhash
or
Ghanaiaian Mbopo-popo-momba

4TH COURSE
Cheeseboard, comprising Latvian Brie, Green Wenslydale,
Paragyan Goatsbladder, Norwegian Stilton, Tartar Mares
Milk Schpludge and Ugandan Cheddar

MICRONESIAN COFFEE AND LICQUEURS

As if trying to eat all that lot wasnt hard enough, I am also deligated to find a complimentary wine-list.

'Nigel's in charge of the wine,' Louise says airily. (I.e. If you want to blame anyone, blame him.)

(This is an example of the latent sexual harrassment from which we men suffer quite a bit. Louise is very good at it. Another example ocurrs regularly when a chicken, turkey ect. is being carved. She will say airily (NB – Any husband about to be sexualy harrased will find that his wife speaks *airily*): 'Nigel, you'd like a leg, *wouldnt you?*' and just because I'm a man I get lumbered with this scrawny old bone while all the ladies are pampered with delicious slivers of breast. Blatent discrimination!)

Anyway, wine, yes – that is reckoned to be 'my department', so I have to pretend to know something about it. Louise presents me with her latest menu and when I have finished gagging I am expected to come up with a selection of wines that will complete a perfect gastrognomic experiense.

Huh.

My personal views on wine can be summed up in two simple rules:

1 It mustnt be sweet (or homemade of course, but that goes without saying).
2 There must be lots of it – no, correction – lots and lots of it.

But Louise still expects me to go through all this garbage about years, vitnages, chateaux botteling, appellation controls ect., and make a big charade of opening bottles, sniffing corks and saying things like, 'I think you'll find this one a bit of a revellation,' to the assembled twits she has invited.

She hopes this will lead to an 'annimated discussion' (Louise's idea of bliss) about how many verukas the middle grape-treader had on his left foot ect., but it rarely does.

(This is due, according to Louise, to my attitude when serving the wine. She reckons shoving a bottle at people and saying, 'Want some paintstripper?' is a deterrant to further conversation.)

You may have got an inkling from the above that I dont like giving (or rather Louise giving) dinner parties.

YOU ARE RIGHT.

The reason is simple – however much you fudge around the issue, a dinner party remains nothing more than a very elaborate way of acumulating a GREAT DEAL OF WASHING-UP.

Mind you, going out to dinner with other people can also have its disadvantages . . . .

THE EGON MOLESWORTH
GOOD FOOD GUIDE

Explanation of symbols

 Distinction

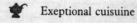 Exeptional cuisuine

Exeptional
wine-list

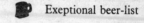 Exeptional beer-list

F-Ts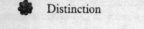

Highly popular with enthusiasts of vegetarianism and macramee, this establishment is greeted less warmly by people who like FOOD. As starters the *brown rice and nettle puré* and the *nut and lentil compost* were found to look like manure and to taste very similar. Also manure-coloured were the main courses, *chickpee and fennelle quishe* and *crustade de leak soya bean tournipe et leaves de nasturtium*. So was the *organic Bulgarian yoguort*. The wines are all estate- (or at least garden-shed-) bottled, and are to be avoided at all costs. The 1983 Dandylion and Burch Bark is perhaps the least reppelent, though that is no reccomendation. The music tends to be Greggorian chant or Equadorian nose-flutes, and the conversation oversweetened. Our Inspector also complaned of too much basil in everything.

CHEZ PEASON 🍺 🍺 🍺 🍺 🍺 🍺 🍺 🍺

A pleasant anex to the Coach and Hounds pub, this attractive *estamminet* provides very welcome traditional English *cuisine*. The cook Sharon's specialities include *sausages*, *chips*, *fried eggs*, *fish fingers*, *beefburgers*, *tomatoe ketchup*, *chips* and quite smutty jokes, and she doesnt mind how long her customers stay in the main building before coming in to eat. Customers are encouraged by mine host to gulp down everything as quickly as possible before getting back next door for another pt. The music tends to be James Last, Abba, Carpenters ect., ect., ect. and the conversation equally undermanding. Our Inspector reccomended Chez Peason as 'the perfect evening out' (though it has to be admitted that his companion found it 'all rather vulgar').

STEVE'S 🍴

'Informal', 'laid-back', 'spaced-out' and 'too much' are all adjectives which have been applied to this unpretensious venue in Notting Hill. The decor, when vizible through the smoke, seems to consist of gram-decks and videorecorders draped with grubby tea-shirts and the ocasional naked woman. Complaints about the service ('If you want a takeaway you can bleeding go out and get it') and the limited wine-list ('There might be a can in the frige') profilerate. The music tends to Very Heavy Metal at Very High Volume and smoking (illegal substances) is compulsery. Generally speaking, in our Inspector's view, 'an aquired taste'.

DARRYLANDCARRYL'S 🥦 🍗 🍾

'Everything absolutely perfect' might well describe an evening in this extrordinarily neat diner. The menu is based exclusively on *Gourmet Cooking To Show Off With* (published by Messrs. Grabber & Grabber in 96 trillion weekly parts), but everything is done with great care. The *salmon mousse, Tornados Rossini* and *cremme broulé* are all excellent. So is the wine-list, though based exclusively on *The Conoissueur of the Bottle Diary* (published by Messrs. Grabber & Grabber @ £7.95). The music tends to be unobtrusive Motzart and Bramhs, based exclusively on *The Right Music For Your Elegant Dinner Party* (published by Messrs. Grabber & Grabber @ £17.95). A serious black mark, though, for the conversation, which tends to circle interminabley around the same topics. Our Inspector's companion found it 'a really elegant evening' and our Inspector himself was rather favourably surprised by the quality (until he found out that the whole thing was a rehearsal for the next week when the Grints were coming).

GRABBER'S

'Not so much a meal as a banquette' was one impressed comment from this lavish extremely pretensious eaterie in Knightsbridge. The Little Woman Who Cooks The Meat does a wonderful *rare beef and vennyson,* and the *aspargus au burre* produced by The Little Woman Who Cooks The Vegetables is 'out of this world'. There have also been favorable comments on the *cavear, smoked salmon, quales in aspic, larks tongues, stuffed peacock, plovvers eggs,* ect., ect. The wine-list matches the food – particularly to be reccomended are the 1840 pre-philloxeria Châteaux Margot and the jerryboams of Dom Perpignan served *comme apperitif.* The 1543 port is also an experiense. Music tends to be the LSO specially booked for the Minstrals Gallery. Our Inspector's only reservation about this unique gasteronomic experiense is that he never gets invited there.

One of the disadvantages of getting older is that, like it or not, ones social life tends to involve an increasing number of FUNCTIONS. These are official ocasions where any potential enjoyment is stopped by the fact that someone gets up and SAYS A FEW WORDS.

As if that werent bad enough, when you get to my age, you sometimes find that YOU are the person who is asked to perform this grisley task.

But do not fear. For all who fear the ghastly moment when this awful request is made to them – HELP IS AT HAND!

The Molesworth all-purpose self-adjusting speech

(Suitable for most ocasions when you are called upon to SAY A FEW WORDS. Simply delete where inaplicable.)

Ladies and gentlemen, when I was asked by

- Bride's father
- Secretary of the Golf Club
- Head of Department
- Rugby Club President

to say a few words, I was very

- honoured,
- weak-minded,
- slow in thinking up an excuse,
- pissed,

so here I am now.

You know, it was a very long time ago when I first met

- the bride.
- today's competition winner.
- Mr —, who's retiring today.
- this old piss-artist.

And let me say – at the risk of causing embarrassment, ha, ha – that at the time

our honoured guest was

- naked on a fur rug.
- swearing in a bunker on the seventeenth.
- a humble clerk in Invoice Docketting.
- pissed as a fiddler's bitch.

Ha, ha, ha.

Well, time passes and now we're
looking at someone who's

{
a married lady.
a surprise club champion.
Assistant Chief Clerk of
Invoice Docketting.
even more pissed.
}

Makes you think, eh? Now this isn't the time for handing out
presents. That's been

done and I'm sure we've
found a good home for

{
all those toast-racks,
the trophy from *my* sideboard,
the engraved barometre,
the inflatable woman,
}

which will be much appreciated. We are here today in honour
of someone who's a . . .

what shall we say?
really good sport,

{
as the bridegroom has
obviously already found out,
in spite of beating me by a
very dubius penalty-stroke,
if we can believe gossip in the
typing pool,
when he can see straight,
}

and someone for whom lie
ahead many happy years of

{
marriage.
cheating.
retirement.
drinking.
}

You know, I'm

not much of a one for telling jokes, but there's a story I heard
recently that rather tickled me – and is quite apt for this occasion. Don't stop me if you've

heard it, ha, ha.
There was this

{
young husband,
golfer from
Aberdeen,
Irishman,
travelling salesman,
}

and he knocked at
the

door of
- his house,
- the caddys room,
- his local chemist,
- this farmhouse,

and the door was opened by
- his new wife,
- one of the caddys,
- the chemist,
- the farmer's daughter,

who was wearing a
- very tearful expression.
- pair of check trousers.
- white coat.
- very transparent nightdress.

So he said,
- 'Is something wrong, darling?'
- 'Are you good at finding golf-balls?'
- 'Do you sell soap?'
- 'Can you put me up for the night?'

and got the reply, 'Yes,
- I made a pie for your supper and the cat's eaten it.'
- I'm very good at finding them.'
- Do you want it scented?'
- My father's away, so you can enjoy any pleasure you want.'

Whereupon he said,
- 'Never mind, love – we can get another cat!'
- 'Right, you find one and then we'll get started!'
- 'No, I'll take it with me!'
- 'Terrific – you mean you've got a dart-board!'

Ha, ha, ha, ha.

Thought you'd like it. Still, that's enough from me. Brevity is the soul of . . . and all

that. But before we
- leave the bride and groom to their own devices,
- re-check today's score-cards,
- allow Mr — one last go at the typing pool,
- start singing 'Eskimo Nell',

her-her,

will you all raise your glasses and drink to
- the bride and groom!
- my getting the trophy back next year!
- boring old —!
- excess!

Thank you very much. (SIT DOWN AMIST WILD APLAUSE.)

4

THE HOME

*Or, Where You Live is an Expression
of YOU*

I remember the day even now.

It was distinctive because I felt relatively AT PEACE and I hadnt even been drinking. It was autum. I was sitting by the gasfire in my unpretensious 3-bdm Wmbldn Frnges semi, and I was semi-comatose, slipping in and out of an idylic dream about Charleen at the office.

Tristram and Lucinda were both out at a party.

My spouse and helpmeat Louise was curled up on the sofa, reading *Some Lesserknown Guatamalan Poems of the Fifteenth Century* (pub. Grabber & Grabber Obscure Books @ £15.95), which was the sort of thing likely to keep her quiet for some time (or at least until the awful moment when she would want to HAVE A SERIOUS DISCUSION WITH ME ABOUT IT – but even she was finding it hard going and was only half-way through, so I reckoned I was safe for a good couple of hours).

I sank back into my reveree. Charleen had just appeared at the door of my Jamaican hotel room, complaning that she couldn't undo the clip at the back of her dress. I pulled my white toweling wrap around my sunburned frame, picked up two *pina colladas* from the bedside table and moved purposfully toward her . . . .

Louise's voice pricks the baloon of my fantesy.

'WE NEED A BIGGER PLACE,' she says.

I gape.

Charleen vanishes like a whisp of smoke in the face of a tournado.*

* Keep on your toes, Booker Prize judges. I am capable of some fairly swish writing when the mood takes me. – Ed.

'Bigger place?' I echo feebley.

'Yes, a bigger place,' says Louise. 'WE NEED A BIGGER HOUSE!'

'ERG,' I respond, as if punched in the sola plexis.

What can she mean? Finally we have reached a kind of financial equilibbrium (i.e. we do not get overdrawn until halfway through each month) and now she wants to ruin it all by taking on bigger morgages, new carpets, curtains, wallpapers, kitchenunits, ect., ect., ect.

'Why?' I ask bewilderd.

'WE NEED MORE SPACE,' she says. 'Besides, the houses up near the Park are a lot more SELECT.' (Oh, I see. Snobbery at the back of it all again. I should have known – snobberys at the back of most things with Louise.)

'But,' I remonstrate feebley, 'we have grown to love this old house.' My voice trembles with emotion. 'It is so full of memories of our early married life and the children when young.* It is like an old friend. We have invested so much time and money and energy into it. It is OUR house – every nook and cranny says "Molesworth" to each spellbound visitor. It is part of ME. It has my unmistakeable stamp all over it.† It is US.'

'NO,' says Louise, 'WE NEED A BIGGER PLACE.'

We wander into an Estate Agents.

They ask us what we want. Louise describes something which is a cross between Blenham Palace and the Ideal Home Exibition.

They ask us how much we can afford. I tell them.

When they have picked themselves up off the floor, they put our name on a list headed '4 bdms, 3 recep' and hand us a sheef of papers.

We wander out.

I vizualise the conversation that follows our departure . . . .

---

* This is, come to think of it, one of the few arguements in favour of moving – Ed.

† i.e. diaganal shelves, wallpaper whose pattens dont match at the ioins, strange fillygree affects in most walls where I have tried to find the joists, ect., ect., ect. – Ed.

IST EST. AGT. O, tht ws fnny!

2ND EST. AGT. Hvnt lghd so mch snce tht old ldys ceiling fll in
the dy aft. shd exchngd cntrcts!!

IST EST. AGT. Fncy hopng to gt 4 bdms, ample acom. + ex-
tens. grnds on an inc. like tht!

2ND EST. AGT. Ys, their fnances are in nd of a lttle imprvmnt,
ha, ha!

IST EST. AGT. Wht shll we do fr thm?

2ND EST. AGT. Hw abt 17 Arbutus Ave?

IST EST. AGT. Ha ha. Wth the dth wtch btle!

2ND EST. AGT. And the rsng dmp! And the subsdnce!

IST EST. AGT. And the mntl hosp. nxt dr!

2ND EST. AGT. And the cr. brkrs yd!

IST EST. AGT. And the abattr!

2ND EST. AGT. Ha ha!

IST EST. AGT. Ha ha!

(Thy bth rll abt on the flr.)

After that of course there's no escape. We are trapped in the
escelating spiral of house purchase and all that entails. Louise
has got the bit between her teeth, so from then on its the Devil
take the Hindmost.

The trouble is that house purchase is one of those things
which show people up in their true colours and since mine are
pale yellow I am not very keen on it.

My commercial abilities are put on the line.

It is a source of continual annoyence to me that SOME
PEOPLE ALWAYS GET BARGAINS AND SOME
DONT. Well no, the real source of annoyence is that I fall into
the second category. And what makes it even more gauling is
the fact that my apalling brother Steve falls into the first.

He has the Midus touch. Everything he touches turns to gold
(whereas everything I touch usually neccesitates my washing
my hands afterwards).

And this has proved true in HOUSE PURCHASE as in
everything else.

TAKE THE BUSINESS OF THE RAFTERS . . . .

Let me present you with two paralell scenes, both involveing
an Estate Agent who combines the seductive power of Salomy
with the morals of Atilla the Hun.

FIRST, the prospective buyer is my apalling brother Steve. He has rolled up to view a Notting Hill house in his new Mercedes, and is dressed in scruffy jeans and a MOTOR-HEAD Tee-shirt. The Oily Estate Agent wheedles him up to the loft . . . .

OILY ESTATE AGENT	These rafters, of course, are more of the house's attractive period features.
STEVE	Dont come that one sunshine. They've been chewed to bits by woodworm.
	(*Thinks:* Does the twit realise that the rafters are clearly rare e.g.s of authentic Jacobian carving on timbers originating from vessels of the Spanish Armada, which will add trillions of pounds to the value of the house?)
O.E.A.	(*who doesnt*) Oh yes. So they have.
STEVE	Which I'm afraid means I'll have to drop my offer on the house by 15 thou.
O.E.A.	(*discomfitted*) Oh really?
STEVE	Yes, and I want a snap decision. Will you accept that offer?
O.E.A.	(*fauning*) Oh . . . cr . . . yes.
STEVE	(*sotto – which he frequently is*) There's one born every minute.

REVIZUALISE the scene now, if you will, with one vital change of personell. Instead of my apalling bro., it is I, Nigel Molesworth, he of the finely-honed commercial acumen, in the roll of Oily Estate Agent's client in the house in Arbutus Avenue.

I have puttered up in my N-registration Avenger and am tastefully attired in a suttle Daks tweed suite, a Marks and Grabber wide-striped, slim-fitting, cotton-polyesther shirt and, of course, the O.C.T. (Old Custardian Tie). Wise to the ways of the breed, I wheedle the Oily Estate Agent up the ladder to the loft.

CHIEF WOODWORM	(*to his hoards of followers who are contentedly munching their midmorning beams*) Cave, chaps! Prospective buyer! Dig in deep! Watch your flight-dust!

ME	*(emerging through trap-door and casting profes-sional eye over rafters)* Ahah! Do I detect the telltale signs of woodworm?
O.E.A.	Don't come that one sunshine.
ME	*(warming to my task)* Then what are all those little holes?
O.E.A.	The former owner was an enthusaistic darts-player.
ME	*(cooling from my task)* Oh really?
O.E.A.	Yes. And anyone who knew anything about it would be able to tell that the rafters have been treated anyway.
ME	*(discomfited, again casting professional eye over rafters)* Oh yes. So they have.
O.E.A.	Now come on. I want a snap decision. Will you offer the asking price?
ME	*(fauning)* Oh . . . er . . . yes. *(O.E.A. whips out contract, which I sign, and pockets my de-posit before we go back down the ladder to discover the dry rot.)*
WOODWORM	*(tutti, before getting their teeth back into what are now my rafters)* There's one born every minute.

'Do you realise,' I say to Louise, in a feeble attemt to deflect her from her kammikhazi course, 'just how much it COSTS to move these days? There's Stamp Duty and removal men and estate agents fees and soliciters and –'

'We can get Basil to act for us,' says Louise. 'Ill have a word with Araminta.'

Oh no, more machinations over the macramee.

'Hear your moving,' says Darryl Pacey in the office at GBH next morning.

How does he manage to know everything? His antaenna must be tuned in to my thought-waves. (UGH – what a ghastly idea. Does he know my innermost thoughts about Charleen at the office? Though, come to think of it, everyone must have the same innermost thoughts about Charleen at the office.)

I grunt equivocaly.

'When Carole and I moved,' says Darryl, 'I did my own conveyanceing.'

Oh yes, you *would*, I think loftily.

'Saved over £750.'

Really? I think less loftily.

I go to the Library that evening and get out a book entitled *Grabbers Guide to Conveyanceing* (pub. Grabber & Grabber Legal Books, price £17.95) and try to read it.

The next morning I ring Basil Fotherington-Thomas.

'Hello, Nigel,' he says. 'How *good* to hear from you.' (He actually *means* it, poor sap.) 'Have you made a will yet?'

'No.'

'Well, you should have done,' he says reproovingly.

I explain that Louise is thinking of moving. I mention Arbutus Ave.

'Oh, *super*,' he says. 'That's much nearer Araminta and me.'

Pain twists in my entrails like a rusty corkscrew.

'Anyway, Nigel,' he continues, 'have you sorted out your finance yet?'

'Er?'

'Finance. Morgage. Have you been to the Building Society yet? Or the Bank?'

'Oh . . . er . . . no.'

'Well, don't you think you should?'

'Oh . . . er . . . yes . . . I suppose so.'

So it's off down the Grabber National Building Society on a BEGGING MISSION, which is, lets face it, DEMEENING.

First I have to join a queueu of smug people who are all depositting lots of money in their Savings Accounts because they are SENSIBLE and SAVEASTHEYEARN. Just like Darrylandcarryl do. In fact, when I look at them, I realise they all look exactly like Darrylandcarryl, which does not improve my mood.

Finally I get to the counter and am greeted by a Bank/Building Society Clerk. All Bank/Building Society Clerks are identical. They are cloaned in some central laboratry (probably in Bracknel – which is the sort of place where the Goverment has secret research stations for that sort of thing). Bank/Building

Society Clerks are all female and talk with an identical South London whine.

THEY ARE ALSO ALL ENGAGED. This is one of the most remarkable discoveries I have made in a not-uneventful life. Every Bank/Building Society Clerk wears a large engagement ring. The reason is obvious – their Young Men have sent them into the Bank/Building Society for the CHEAP MORGAGES.

But the interesting question is: What happens to them when they get married? They disappear. You never see a married one. Maybe they all leave instantly to have babies. Or perhaps they adhear to the view that their PLACE IS AT HOME and practice dusting and polishing nick-nacks all day.

Anyway this engaged Bank/Building Society Clerk greets me and asks what I want.

'Erm . . . I wanted to borrow some money,' I mouthe.

'Sorry. You'll have to speak up.'

By now the eyes of the massed Darrylandcarryls are all fixed on me. 'I'd like to borrow some money,' I repeat, slightly louder.

'Oh, you mean you want a morgage,' the Bank/Building Society Clerk shouts. 'Are you a Regular Saver with the Society?'

I confess that I am not, to a ripple of tutting from the assembled Darrylandcarryls. Disapproving, the Bank/Building Society Clerk fixes me an appointment with the Morgage Application Dept.

When I turn up for this I am treated as if what I am asking for is slightly obsene, as if I've GOT A BIT OF NERVE to want to borrow money.

This really gets up my goat. It's mugs like me who give the Building Societies all the trillions of pounds which they sit on, so I think they should treat us with a bit of respect. Or at least treat ME with a bit of respect. It is a sad fact, and a baffling one, that petty officials seldom show any recognition for my INTRINSIC BREEDING.

Anyway they eventually agree to lend me the money. Mind you, I have to go through more disapproving looks and tutting. I don't understand why. The contract I eventually sign is completely one-sided. They take over everything I own for the next twenty-five years and all I seem to get out of it is the right to pay them exorbitent amounts of money.

There is no justice.

So it is that we end up living in 17, Arbutus Ave, Wimbledon.

Our moving in is the signal for three things to happen instantaniously:

1 The house next door to our old house (identical in every particular) is sold for twice as much as we got.
2 The cieling of the kitchen in the new house falls in.
3 The morgage rate goes up 2%.

Oh well, ç'et la vie.

The trouble is it doesnt stop there. Moving in is only the beginning.

Having said on first seeing the house that it is EXACTLY WHAT SHE HAS ALWAYS WANTED, as soon as we're there Louise sets about CHANGING EVERYTHING IN SIGHT. It is with considerable reluctance that she allows the bricks to stay in their original order.

I think that the house is mororless all right as it is, but my views are ignored. Nor does Louise get on with it on her own and just relie on me to pay the bills. Although she sets ABSOLUTELY NO STORE by my opinion, she insists on CONSULTING ME ABOUT EVERYTHING.

(I dont think its actualy ME she wants, just anything that'll listen. I have contemplated setting up a taperecorder to say Yes, Really? Well . . . Yes, Yes, ect. at stated intevals, but I'm afraid she might notice.)

The result is I get dragged down to Grabbers Home Decor Dept. to look at wallpapers ect. 'Don't you think the red flowers are a bit too cottagey for the Guest Room, Nigel? Do you prefer the pale blue? This one would set off that washstand we inheritted from Aunty Stella, wouldn't it? Do you think this embossed effect is too like an Indian restaraunt? Is the pink a bit chintzie? What do you THINK, Nigel?'

ERGH . . . .

The answer is that I dont THINK anything.

It is not the sort of subject on which I have THOUGHTS.

My only concern with walls is that they STAND UP (something I do not yet feel confidant about at No 17, Arbutus Ave). What covers them is a matter of complete indifference to me.

I hope to get by with 'Yes', which is usually fine when dealing with Louise, but on this sort of ocasion it is inadaquate. 'Your not being any HELP, Nigel. You want this to be a MUTUAL DECISION, don't you, Nigel?'

('Why suddenly change the habits of a lifetime?' I think of replying, but I dont have the bottle.)

The trouble is that all this doesnt stop when we get home. After Grabbers Home Decor Dept. all I want to do is sit down with a beer and watch snooker or something equally undermanding on the television.

BUT I AM NOT ALLOWED TO.

Instead I am dragged round the house, being asked about the paintwork. 'I thought the Burnt Paella in the hall, didn't you, Nigel? Do you think the Blushing Oyster would be better? Though actually that Saharian Shimmer was nice, wasnt it? Or did you like the Congo Caramelle? Or the Scorched Saffron? Or the Tanned Flesh? Go on, Nigel, do say – what do you THINK?'

Once again I have NO VIEWS.

The thing that worries me about all this is that these are only the preliminery skirmishes. Once Louise has made the decisions and bought everything, not only will I be crippled financialy, I will also be expected to ACTUALY PUT THE WALL-PAPER UP AND PAINT ALL THIS PAINTWORK.

In a word – DO-IT-YOURSELF, Nigel!

ERGH . . . .

DO-IT-YOURSELF goes against every principal that I hold dear. So long as there is one other person alive in the world I will see to it that he DOES-IT-HIMSELF rather than me DOING-IT-MYSELF.

However there is a snag – other people DOING-IT-FOR-YOU expect to be PAID MONEY.

So, with heavy brow and muttered curses, I – even I, Nigel Molesworth – am sometimes to be seen scaling ladders clutching cieling tiles and adeshive, or bent over my Black and Grabber Workmate, wondering what on earth *The Grabbers Digest Book Of Being Awfully Good At That Sort Of Thing* (pub. by Grabber & Grabber @ £11.95) means by 'dovetailed rebates'.

Ocasionally, given a specific project, I can get quite absorbed. Louise will say, 'Tristram's room is a complete tip and will be till he has some shelves for his books comix model areoplanes casettes ect., ect., there are some nice ones at Grabbers only £32,' wherupon I say, 'Ridiculous price no that's the sort of thing I can do much cheaper,' and go down to Grabbers Timber Dept. where I pay £10 for a few measley planks, on to their Do-It-Yourself Dept. where I pay £5 for polyuerothane varnish ect., ect., ect., before remembering that my saw hasn't been the same since Tristram left it in the paddeling pool for a fortnight and buying a new saw, hammer, chisle, spirit level, plain, screwdriver ect. for £18.

I take my purchases home and now its the old primoeval battle of MAN against WOOD, each pitting his grain against the other. The Molesworth Daydream-Service takes over.

1ST CONOISSUEUR	Egad! That's a remarkably fine piece of furniture.
2ND CONOISSUEUR	Ecod, yes! It looks like a Molesworth.
1ST CONOISSUEUR	Pshaw! Ha, ha, that'll be the day, when we find an origianal Molesworth. There's so much reproduction stuff about
2ND CONOISSUEUR	But those lines – the distinctive fluted beading, the beaded fluting, the dovetailed rebates – odd's my life, it has all the hallmarks of the Genius himself!
1ST CONOISSUEUR	Tish!
2ND CONOISSUEUR	Bless you.
1ST CONOISSUEUR	Nay, tish and pish! If twere a genuine Molesworth twould go for trillions of pounds at Sothebys.
2ND CONOISSUEUR	But look! Their's a carving on the underside! The crossed chisles! The trademark of Nigel Molesworth himself! It's –

At this point I make my own actual trade mark – a slipped chisle which splits the entire plank – and the dream fades.

All Louises going-on-at-me when we moved made me ask myself whether I ever had thought about DECOR at all.

I came to the conclusion that I hadnt – at least I hadnt thought about it for ME, though I had observed other peoples

STYLES and do apreciate how DECOR CAN BE A REVEL-
LATION OF CHARACTER. E.g. . .

THE FOTHERINGTON-THOMASES seem to be trying to
get back to some sort of pasteural iddyl which I dont think ever
existed. They frolick around like nimphs and shepherds in front
of Laura Ashely wallpapers and generally try to make their
home deny that they live in the suburbs. They no sooner look
at a piece of furniture than they strip it. They have this big
Victorian house and their aim is to make the inside look as like
a cowshed as possible. The Laura Ashely bits are the milking
parlor, but elsewhere there is lots of darkbrown paint, strippedpine, old agricultural implements stuck on the wall ect. The
result in my view is quite revoltingly precsious and prissy (so
thats in character).

DARRYLANDCARRYL'S modern town-house has got pellmets on everything and where it hasnt got pellmets its got little
psuedo-Georgian wiggly bits of decoration stuck on all the doors
cuboards ect. Everything is in pale green, baige and other
insipid colours.
    They even have a wraughtiron drinks trolly. (Can humankind
dessend lower than that?)
    Its all unbelievabley neat. Carole goes round every hour on
the hour with eyebrow tweezers stalking specks of dust.
    Huh. Just wait till they have children (though no doubt their
children will be as neat and hygenic as deepfrozen chickens in
polythene).
    Anyway the decor fits them all right.

TIMOTHY PEASON does not notice his environement (he
doesnt notice much actualy) so the decor is all Sharon's doing.
Louise hints darkly that this is NOT A GOOD THING. She
does not approve of Rasberry Ripple carpets, veneered coffee
tables with gold legs, dangley frosted snowflake lightfittings,
orange loovered cuboard doors, luminous paintings of sunsets
on black velvet and displays of coloured glass animals on every
surface.
    My view is more tollerant. For me the atmosphere of a house
is created not by the taudry semblances of outward show (!) but

by the attitudes of those who dwell therein, and since Timothy and Sharon Peasons attitude is to offer me a beer on arrival then their decor is ALL RIGHT BY ME.

THE MOLESWORTH GUIDE TO HOME MAINTAINANCE

An Easy-to-Follow alphabettical list of Jobs to be Done around the House

Key: P = Peasy E = Easy B = Boring D = Difficult
ED = Extremely Difficult LM = Get in a Little Man

BRICKLAYING [LM] Walls are distressingly permenant structures. The only one I ever built (on the end of the pattio) has always looked as if its about to fall down but unfortunatley never does. This means Peason still has a good laugh whenever he comes round. Its very hurtful.

CEMENTING [P + ED] Mixing cement is P and quite fun; doing anything with it once its mixed is ED.

CHAINSAWING [E] Using a chainsaw is fun and gives one an attavistic sense of power. Even better, you can imagine what you're sawing is Grint or Darryl Pacey. But only do it for 5 mins; after that the novelty wears off and it becomes HARD WORK.

CHANGING LIGHTBULBS [E] I do this.

CHANGING FUSES [E] Louise does this.

CIELING TILES [D + B] Who wants tiles on their cieling anyway? (The answer is, unfortunatley, Louise.)

DAMP [ED] There is only one rule about damp and that is: THE SOURCE IS NEVER WHERE YOU THINK IT IS.

DEMOLITION [P] Great fun, particularly with something big like a wall. Swinging a sledgehammer releases fantesies that you are Thaw, Tarzan, Superman ect. As in CHAINSAWING (q.c.), you can also imagine the wall is Grint or Darryl Pacey. (NB. It is important to DO SOMETHING TO YOUR BACK or FEEL A PAIN IN

YOUR CHESTAL AREA as you knock out the last brick. This ensures that someone else has to clear up the mess.)

DRILLING [E]   Being handy with the old Black and Grabber electric drill is actualy fataly E. It has led me to propound (classy word, eh?) MOLESWORTH'S LAW OF DRILLING, which goes as follows: EVERY HOLE IN THE CORRECT PLACE SHALL BE SUROUNDED BY AT LEAST THREE OTHER HOLES WHICH WERE EARLIER ATTEMPTS TO FIND THE RIGHT PLACE.

FINISHING [B]   1 Covering wood with polyuerothane varnish. Doing it the first time is OK, but your meant to wait for that lot to dry, sand it down, put on another coat ect. about a trillion times. That is the B bit. (Nothing in our house has got more than one coat of anything.)

[P]   2 Downing tools with the SATISFACTION OF A JOB WELL DONE and nipping down the Coach and Hounds for a couple of pts.

FLOOR TILES [D + B]   One of those sickning jobs where you have to GET IT RIGHT otherwise you resent it every time you trip over. When the subject is mentioned, suggest carpet, linolium, going to the pub ect.

GLAZING [ED]   This is constantly required because Tristram keeps kicking footballs ect. through windows. Experiense of mending them has led me to formulate MOLESWORTH'S RULES OF GLAZING, which are: 1 NINE TIMES OUT OF 10 THE MESUREMENTS OF THE PIECE OF GLASS YOU GOT FROM THE GLACIER WONT CORRESPOND TO THOSE OF THE APPERTURE WHEN YOU GET IT HOME.

2 ON THE RARE OCASIONS WHEN THE PIECE OF GLASS IS THE SAME SIZE YOU WILL BREAK IT BEFORE YOU'VE FINISHED FITTING IT.

GROUTING [E]   This is actualy quite fun so long as someone else has put up the tiles you've got to grout.

GUTTERING [E, but B, so LM]   This should be cleaned out regularly, but you wont catch me doing it.

HANGING A DOOR [ED]   There is no point in trying to do

this. It wont work and the door will swing drunkenly on its hinges and look accusingly at you for the rest of your life. (So will Louise.)

INSULATION [LM]   The only interesting thing about insulation is that its supposed to cut down your heating bills, but because heating prices are always going up you never notice the diffrence so it soon ceases to be interesting.

PAINTING [B]   The important thing is to cover up anything that might get splashed but since doing that is even more B than the actual painting, one tends not to. (I thought the piano looked nice the same blue as the cieling anyway. Louise didnt.)

PAPERHANGING [B]   In fact incredibly B. It is also quite D, even when the wallpaper is all one colour. (NB – HAVE NO TRUCK with anything thats got a pattern – that's definately LM.)

PAVING [D + B]   See FLOOR TILES (q.c.).

PLASTERING [LM]   Far too difficult for someone like me. GETTING PLASTERED on the other hand is far too easy. (A Cheap Joke inserted for Timothy Pearson's benefit – its about his level.)

PLUMMING [LM]   Definately LM.

REPARING CHINA [ED]   This never works so its not worth bothering to try.

REPLACING TAP WASHERS [EED]   This is impossible.

REWIRING [LM]   Only to be attemted when you're tired of life.

ROOF REPAIRS [LM]   Only a nut would try to do his own roof repairs. (Darryl Pacey does – need I say more?)

STRIPPING [B]   Taking the paint off the bannisters is one of those things Louise makes sound E. Do not be fooled. If you've got a blowlamp the first bit can be fun, esp. the fantesies (cf. CHAINSAWING and DEMOLITION). But thereafter the whole thing goes downhill. Rubbing away interminibly with sandpaper is a pretty fatuous waste of a fine mind like mine and people who do enjoy it (e.g. Basil and Araminta Fotherington-Thomas) must be pretty peculier (Q.E.D.). If *really* want something stripped, send it off to an ACID BATH. (That can promt some fairly tasty fantesies about Grint and Darryl Pacey too.)

VYNIL WALLPAPER [ED]   HAVE NO TRUCK WITH THIS. As if hanging the ordinary stuff werent hard enough, vynil wallpaper is ELASTIC (a practical joke on behalf of the manufacturors which I regard as beneath contempt).

WORKSHOP, FITTING OUT [P]   The most important equipment the home handiman recquires in his workshop is a few cans of beer, a casette player, some back numbers of Forum and A LOCK ON THE DOOR SO THAT LOUISE CANT COME IN UNNANOUNCED.

5

THE OFFICE

*Or, How to be a Subleiutenant
of Industry*

As you will probably have worked out by now (if your reading this book from the beginning – and theres no reason why you should), I work for GBH (Grabber Bulk Holdings) in the Invoice Docketting Department.

In fact that is not the whole story. I work for Invoice Docketting (Internal), never to be confused with Invoice Docketting (External) a department between whom and us (grammer) there exists a deep rivalrey.

The Head of Invoice Docketting (Internal) – and therefor my boss – is Grint. Darryl Pacey (of Darrylandcarryl) also works in the dept. at the same level (CJ2/B) as me (despite being nearly ten years younger, FUMES OF JEALOUSY).

There are various other gnomes about the eleventh floor of GBH House but the most significant other members of the department are two secretaries called Celia and Charleen.

Celia is significant because she is unbelievabley classy.

Charleen is significant because she is unbelievabley sexy.

CHARLEEN is the sort of girl who it is not fair to leave around an office full of normal men (or even our office, come to that). Even that swot Darryl Pacey has been known to pause in his dictation when she walks into the room.

She has an amazing figure and dresses to accentuate it. She favours shiny materials which leave no doubt as to her contures. Everything she wears conforms to the CHARLEEN TWO-INCH RULE. (If the fashion is for short skirts, Charleens will be two inches shorter; if the fashion is for low cleaviges, hers will be two inches lower.)

She does things like dieing her hair purple, painting her fingernails black and hanging scrapmetal from her ears to draw attension to herself. This is all WASTED EFFORT. Attension is drawn to her quite naturaly, but not to her hair, fingernails or ears.

She is about seventeen and has absolutely 0 between her ears. But no one looks between her ears. Too busy looking between the other bits.

CELIA too is not without allure. Shes not so obviously (indeed BLATENTLY) attractive from the purely phisical point of view, but the thought of all that BREEDING is profoundly affrodisiac. She also talks in this sexy deb quack.

I often think I missed my vacation as a Debs Delight.

The Molesworth Daydream-Service takes over . . .

(Nigel de Vere Chomlondly Featherstonhawe Von Trapp Battenburg Sachertorte Molesworth (the Rt. Hon.) is at the Rt. Hon. Letaetia Snure-Dobley's coming-out ball at the Dorchester. A group of adoring Sloane Rangers, dripping with family jewells, suround him)

NIGEL ECT. ECT.	*(concluding an anicdote)* . . . turned out his polo pony's withers were twisted all the time!
SLOANE RANGERS	*(tutti)* Hwa, hwa, hwa, Oh, Nigel, you are a one, You ought to be on television, ect., ect., ect.
NIGEL ECT. ECT.	I'm finding this ball a bit of a bore.
S.R.S	*(tutti)* Hwa, hwa, Oh Nigel, you are so witty, ect.
NIGEL ECT.	I was thinking of tootling over to Anabelles for a quick frisko at the disco.
S.R.S	*(tutti)* Hwa, hwa, hwa, Oh Nigel, you are so clever, And so sexy, Let me drive you there in my Porsche, You can have me anytime, Why don't we nip up to Deddy's flat in St James's Palace, ect., ect., ect.

I don't know. I suppose it might pale after a bit.

HOW TO GET THE BEST OUT OF YOUR SECRETARY
(For Office Parties see Ch. 11)

I will own up straight away – I have never had a secretary all to myself. I have to share the services of Celia and Charleen with Darryl Pacey and a few other gnomes. My share works out at about 33.333333% of Celia and 17.2943% of Charleen (though if one takes into account the amount of Charleen's mind that is actually thinking about her work at any given time, the figure is nearer 0.00000000000000000000000000000000000 0000000000000000000000001%).

Nonetheless I have in my time at GBH observed many secretaries at work and know a great deal about the breed. And I am prepared to share a little of my expertease with you.

It has been said by a wiser mind than mine (yes, o gentle reader, such do exist) that the relationship between BOSS and SECRETARY is like a MARRIAGE, and indeed secretaries do fall into many of the same categaries as WIVES. The following are all quite common:

EARTHMOTHERS	Who see it as their job to LOOK AFTER their boss, brush dandrough from his shoulders, ect.
TWITTERING WORRIERS	Who live in fear of running out of paperclips.
OFFICE GAULEITERS	Whose bosses have to knock befor going into their own offices and who correct typing errors just by looking at them.
HIGH ACHEEVERS	Who are GOING ON TO GREATER THINGS: they finish their work by 9.30 a.m. and spend the rest of the day filling in job aplications.
WHINGEING LIBBERS	Who regard being asked to type a letter as Sexual Harassment.
SEXPOTS	Well, theres Charleen.

Of course there are lots of secretaries just like Carole of Darrylandcarryl, who never talk about anything but the office, who's entire social life revolves round the company choir, badminton club, brassrubbing group, hanggliding society ect. and who's holidays are taken with the company travel club.

Another paralell between Secretaries and Wives is that the relationship NEVER WORKS OUT AS WELL AS YOU THOUGHT IT WOULD.

The important thing with secretaries is to let them know WHO'S BOSS, you or she. And once you have decided that (some people favour tossing for it), stick to your role. It is very confusing for a boss whose used to being in charge suddenly to have his secretary volunteiring an idea, or for one who is used to having his secretary organising everything to be suddenly called upon to DO SOMETHING OFF HIS OWN BAT. Thats the kind of thing that leads to coronornaries.

The quality of a secretary can be gauged by the way in which she answers her boss's telephone. Here are the main methods:

1	THE PROPERLY SUBSERVIANT	'Mr Molesworth's office.'
2	THE DISCLAIMING	'Mr Molesworth's phone.'
3	THE UNECCESARILY HONEST	'Mr Molesworth, Mr Pacey and a few other gnomes' phone.'
4	THE COSILY INFORMAL	'Nigel's.'
5	THE DETERENT	'Yes?'
6	THE FRANKLY RUDE	'What do *you* want?'
7	THE PREOCUPIED	'Hang on – I'm talking to my friend.'
8	THE NEW TEMP	'Mr Molesomething's office.'
9	THE I-SHOULD-BE-SO-LUCKY	'Mr Molesworth's lap.'

You can also judge secretaries by the excuses they make when your phone rings at 10 to 3 and your still in the Kings Arms.
Here are the Top Ten Excuses:

1 'I'm afraid Mr Molesworth is in an important meeting.'
2 'I'm afraid Mr Molesworth is unavailable.'
3 'I'm afraid Mr Molesworth has not yet returned from an important meeting.'
4 'I'm afraid Mr Molesworth has not yet returned from an important luncheon meeting.'
5 'I'm afraid Mr Molesworth has not yet returned.'
6 'I'm afraid Nigel isn't back from lunch yet.'

7 'Oh, he's not back *yet*.'
8 'Huh. Well I suppose he might be back later – you never know your luck.'
9 'What, catch Nigel back before halfpast three – you gotta be joking!'
10 'He's still at the Kings Arms and probably pissed by now.'

(It has never been my good fortune to have the services of a secretary who appeared to know of the existence of Nos 1–5.)

If you do sometimes have the use of a secretary there are certain office skills you have to develop. Among them is DICTATING.

If your not good at it you can be SHOWN UP and no subleiutenant of industry can afford to be SHOWN UP. The aim is always to apear cool and in control. This means you have to be supremely arcticulate as you create letters, memos ect. spontaniously out of the air. Your secretary will be a witness of any hesitancy, solescism or lapse of grammer.

(Darryl Pacey never actually dictates to a secretary in person. He is such a swot that he comes into the office at 5 a.m. every morning and does all his letters into a tape-recorder so that they dont interfere with the days work. URGH. Needles to say, what he records is supremely arcticulate anyway FUMES OF JEALOUSY).

If you can dictate well (i.e. without too many ums, ers, scrub thats ect.) do not waste it on your secretary. As with all things in an office that you are good at, MAKE SURE SOMEONE ELSE SEES YOU BEING GOOD AT IT.

A popular wheeze is to be *discovered* dictating. If you have got letters, memos ect. to be done, wait until you know someone's about to come in (e.g. the Commisionairre from Reception has just rung through to say someones on his way). With a little practise you can judge how long it takes them to get up to the eleventh floor and so guage the exact moment to start so that they will arrive to find you *in flagrante dictatio*. (But watch out for the ones who stop at the GENTS on their way up.)

(Insidentally, another good wheeze when someone is due to see you is to phone your extention number up from one of the other phones in the room so that yours is ringing when they come in. These little subtefuges all help to create around you an aura of busy efficiancy.)

WALKING ROUND THE ROOM WHILE DICTATING is O.K. (even quite smooth), but it is UNPROFFESIONAL to look over your secretarys shoulder when you lose your thread. This is for two reasons:

1 You can't read shorthand so looking at what she's written so far wont help.
2 If its Charleen youll find your looking straight down her cleavage and any chance of getting your thread back goes out the window.

TRY AND RATION HOW OFTEN YOU SAY 'COULD YOU READ THAT BACK TO ME?' as this is a sign of weakness.

But do be careful to check what she's written from time to time. Some secretaries take their duties very literally and will take down ABSOLUTELY EVERYTHING you say.

The result could be memos like the following:

From etcetera, Extension well you know that, To etcetera and his Room Number, Date what is it the 7th oh no the 8th thats right, Subject this boring boring business about the proposed change of departmental name. Right what shall I say to the slimey toad? Yes O.K. just a min I'm going to blow my nose. *PROOSCH!* Right where was I oh yes with regard to your um er no scrub that in response to your memo of what was the date on his well have a look. Well I don't know perhaps you went against the habits of a lifetime and filed it no I'm sorry I didn't mean that oh God please don't cry look here's my handkerchief oh you poor little thing. I'm not really an ogre you know if you got to know me better you'd find . . . . Maybe we could meet for a drink one evening and ooh youve got nice soft shoulders and lovely hair and its sad to see tears in those beautiful eyes and . . . . Right where were we yes O.K. in response to your memo of yesterdays date I'm not sure that this is the time for major changes. Um. Er. My wife doesnt undestand me you know its a long time since our marriage has been a marriage in more than name but I get the feeling that you undestand me in a way that OH HELLO BILL didn't hear you come in just er just er Miss Evans had a thread caught on her blouze. What a drink in the King's Arms after work smashing idea see you there then round five thirty right where was I? Oh yes . . . festina lente. Lente L-E-N-T-E its Latin oh it means dont rush things yes fine

66

Latin'll confuse the little erk didnt do Latin at his grubby secondery modern ha ha. O.K. if you could type that up then Ill sign it before I sneak off to the K.A. well its after eleven they'll be open and at least I'll feel I've done something this morning.

MEMOS

Memos are a subj. in themselves and one on which I am a bit of an expert. Let me share some of my wrinkles with you (God knows I can spare them).

The basic aim of all memos is maximum confusion. If you can insure that you get something into the In-Tray of a colleague (preferably a senior colleague) which really flummoxxes him, then your day has not been completely wasted.

At GBH memos are much used in the continuing war of attrition between Invoice Docketting (Internal) and Invoice Docketting (External).

Though it hurts me to say it, Grint is very good at them. He can really set the cat among the pigeons by unleashing something like this:

FROM: Head of Invoice Docketting (Internal)	EXT. : 4071
TO: Head of Invoice Docketting (External)	DATE : 6th May
SUBJECT : Departmental Names	

I propose that we change the names of Invoice Docketting (Internal) and Invoice Docketting (External) to Dockett Invoicing (Internal) and Dockett Invoicing (External) respectively. Reaction?

C.de V. J. Grint
HEAD OF INVOICE DOCKETTING (INTERNAL)

This proposal will cause great constenation in the office of the Head of Invoice Docketting (External) who will be FURIOUS THAT HE DIDNT THINK OF IT FIRST and therefore oppose it on principal.

In his reply he is likely to use one of the great memo-sending ploys – EXTENDING THE DISTRIBUTION LIST.

The principal is very simple. Basicly you should send all memos to as many people as possible, *particularly those who have nothing to do with the subj.*

This serves 3 functions:

1 It makes the irelevent people on the distribution list feel important.
2 It wastes time because some of them will feel called upon to reply.
3 (AND MOST IMPORTANT) It worries the person to whom the memo is addressed.

The result of using the method is this sort of thing:

FROM : Head of Invoice Docketting (External)   EXT. : 4721
TO : Head of Invoice Docketting (Internal)   DATE : 7th May
cc.   Assistant Head of Invoice Docketting (External)
      Assistant Head of Invoice Docketting (Internal)
      Cheif Clerk, Invoice Docketting (External)
      Cheif Clerk, Invoice Docketting (Internal)
      Assistant Cheif Clerk, Invoice Docketting (External)
      Assistant Cheif Clerk, Invoice Docketting (Internal)
      Administrative Assistant, Invoice Docketting (External)
      Administrative Assistant, Invoice Docketting (Internal)
      External Invoice Docketting Organiser
      Internal Invoice Docketting Organiser
      Head of Catering (Manchester)
      Cheif Stationary Buyer (Littlehampton)
      All Output Monitoring Staff
      Quality Control (Kew)
      Assistant Head of Memo Disposal
      Organiser, Retrospective Planning
      Despatch Coordinater
      Sales Inhibitor (Domestic)
      Boilerman (Central Premisses)
      Boilerman's Dog
      Office Cleaners*
SUBJECT: Proposed change of names of Invoice Docketting (External) and Invoice Docketting (Internal) to Dockett Invoicing (External) and Dockett Invoicing (Internal) respectively.

No.   J. C. Smythe
                 HEAD OF INVOICE DOCKETTING (EXTERNAL)

---

* Who are going to read it anyway, so may as well be put on the distribution list – Ed.

These two salvos declare hostillities well and truly open. Now anyone can contribute to the crossfire and this is the point when I – even I, Nigel Molesworth – may be tempted to join the fray. I am likely to add the aditional refinement of INITIALS which profilerate in all offices. E.g. . . . .

FROM : N.M.		EXT. : 4227
TO : A.H.I.D.(I)		DATE : 8th May
cc. H.I.D.(I)	D.V.	
H.I.D.(E)	C.O.D.	
A.H.I.D.(E)	L.S.O.	
C.C.I.D.(I)	S.P.C.K.	
C.C.I.D.(E)	P.L.J.	
A.C.C.I.D.(I)	D.T.	
A.C.C.I.D.(E)	Y.M.C.A.	
A.A.I.D.(I)	I.O.W.	
A.A.I.D.(E)	T.N.T.	
E.I.D.O.(I)	O.C.	
E.I.D.O.(E)		

SUBJECT.: I.D. or D.I.?

I.D.:A.1.,D.I.:N.B.G.. R.S.V.P.a.s.a.p.

N.

P.S. G + T in K.A. 5.30 p.m?

This sort of thing can go on for *months*.

Insidentally, if you do inadvertantly miss someone out of a distribution list, there is nothing easier than RETRASPEC- TIVE FORGERY of a carbon of the original, suitably amended.

'Sorry old boy, no, of course I don't think you're lying, but it's here in black and white. You definately should have had a copy. Must be the Internal Post.'

(NB – The Internal Post can be blamed for anything that goes wrong in an office. So can The Computer. Or the Office Cleaners.)

Of course you needn't stop at forging distribution lists. Go the whole hog – forge complete memos. Carbon-dating may be pretty sophisticated, but nobody's going to be able to prove that you did the carbon of a memo this afternoon rather than on the date at the top of the page.

(But NB – Beware of changes in office stationary. If new-shaped memo-forms came in three months after your supposed original, you can look pretty silly. And also NB Try to type the forgery yourself. And if you really *have* to use a secretary, make sure its one on whom you've got something incriminating – i.e. keep your Polaroid handy at the Office Party.)

Before we leave the subj. of memos, I would like to mention my own favourite device, THE UNRELATED MEMO.

This is garuanteed to send your colleague (or lets call a spade a spade – enemy) rushing to his filing cabinet to search out the previous links in a non-existant chain of correspondance. E.g.

FROM : N. Molesworth   EXT.: 4227
TO : A.H.I.D.(E)   DATE : Whenever
SUBJECT : Recent proposal
Sure you know best, but think you may be taking a risk. Still, on your own head be it.

                                        N. Molesworth

Recieving a memo like that can ruin someone's whole morning.

One of the main problems in all offices (and particulerly on the 11th floor of GBH House) is how to fill the time.

There are of course the obvious ways – sending obstructive memos, chatting up Charleen, reading Forum in the Gents, flicking paperclips with rubberbands, getting the Palace gossip from Celia, making complex structures out of pollystyreen coffee cups, having long lunch hours in the Kings Arms, sticking down the black buttons on Darryl Paceys telephone with sellotape ect., ect., ect. – but that is not enough to bridge the acheing void betw. 10 and 6.

So inevitabley one has to resort to FANTESY.

90 per cent of my office fantesies are of course about Charleen, but different ones can ocasionally be unleashed by other articles of office equippment.

E.g. some weeks back I made a discovery. It was that SOMETHING HAPPENS TO GBH INTERNAL ENVELOPES BEFORE THEY REACH THE NATURAL END OF THEIR USEFUL LIFE.

Let me ellucidate. GBH Internal Envelopes are large buff jobs with a string at the back to tie them, stern injunctions not to use staples, and on the front 24 numbered boxes saying:

NAME ....

DEPARTMENT ....

ROOM NUMBER ....

The idea is that they get used and go back and fourth timeand-timeagain until all 24 boxes have been filled.

But I suddenly realised that I HAD NEVER SEEN ONE WITH MORE THAN 5 BOXES USED!!!!!!

This was enough. Instantly my finely-developped imaginative machinery clicked into gear . . .

THE CASE OF THE MISSING ENVELOPES

It was a slate-gray Thursday, mid-afternoon, London. Rain played rhythm on the window-glass of the office. A blinking neon outside pulsed colours across the floor. My powder-blue trousers were on the desk, with my legs inside them. I raised the afternoon's ninth cigarette to my lips and an eyebrow to the opening door.

The dame who opened it could have been lovely on another day in another place. But now the dark waves were flattenned to her skull by the rain, and the big slate-gray eyes were too big. She looked as scared as a skittle in an ally.

'Are you Nigel Molesworth?' she gasped.

I nodded, leaving my power-blue trousers on the desk, with my legs inside them.

'You got to help me. Your the only person who can.'

She was right. I was the only person who could. I talked money. A hundred and fifty a day. Plus expenses. She gave me a thousand on account. She didnt say on account of what.

I asked her problem. She hesitated, gave herself a little shake, then out it came, like ketchup from a bottle. And it looked just as bloody.

I didnt move. My power-blue trousers stayed on the desk, with my legs inside them. I cremated the afternoon's tenth cigarette. And the eleventh. And the twelth. And the thirteenth. She had a lot to say.

She stopped. Her face was slate-gray. She still looked as scared as a stuffed olive at a coctail party.

I chewed my lip, then spat it out. 'You figure someone takes the envelopes?'

'You got any other explainations?'

I had a few cooking but they needed a little longer in the oven.

'Used five times, then they dissapear?' I asked her.

STAFF HOLIDAYS CHART

	JAN	FEB	MAR	APR	MAY	JUN	JUL	AUG	SEP	OCT	NOV	DEC
GRABBER	ST. MORTIZ			ST. LUCIA		ST. TROPPEZ				SEYSHELLES		ST. M
GRINT			CAIRO		TOKYO		DORDONGE				ROME	LA
PACEY		MANAGEMENT TRAINING COURSE				COMPUTER COURSE			ACCOUNTANCY COURSE		TRAINING COURSE	
CELIA	ST. MORTIZ		SANDRINGHAM			ASCOT, WELLS, ROTHERHAM	GOOD-WOOD ECT.	JAMAICA		SIR LANAKA		BALMORAL
CHARLEEN	ALPS – NUDE SKIING					CORFUE – NUDE SUNBATHING			MASARIA – NUDE SUNBATHING			
MOLESWORTH				* QLD				ROSE-HNGHN – L.M.			* W.D	* L.M

* W.D. = Wimbledon, decorating L.M. = Louise's Mother (Ugh – Ed.)

She nodded. It would have been a nice nod if it had been consenting to something else.

'Anyone you suspect?'

This nod was shorter, like a bad edit in a censered film.

'Name?'

'Grint.'

My powder-blue trousers moved from the horrizontal to the vertical plain. My legs followed suit.

I repeated the name. 'Grint.'

Slap on cue the door opened. He stood there, as welcome as half a maggott in an apple. My hand jumped to the desk draw. The gun nesled in my palm like an old lover remet in a Paris hotel.

'Something I can do for you, Grint?'

'YES, MOLESWORTH, YOU CAN STOP LOOKING OUT OF THAT BLOODY WINDOW AND GET ME THOSE FIGURES ON MEMO DISPOSAL REALOCATION!!!! AND WHAT THE HELL ARE YOU DOING WITH THAT RULER IN YOUR HAND??!!??!!??!!??!!??!!??!!??!!'

(You know, he *is* like my old headmaster, Grimes.)

Anyway, I'm afraid most of my office fantesies end that way. So its back to my mesmorised study of Charleen's cleavige. Am I, I wonder, really becoming a DIRTY OLD MAN?

6

DRESS

Or, Who Cares What the Smart Young Executive is Wearing?

OFFICEWEAR

SUITS. Unfortunatley Grint expects the men in Invoice Dock-etting (Internal) to wear SUITS which is pretty boring just like being back at school, chiz ect.

I have two suits. One is MORE TRADITIONAL (i.e. INCREDIBLY OLD, the sort of suit my father might have worn. In fact I think he did). It is CHARCOAL in colour, with a DISCRETE CHALK STRIPE and when I wear it in Grabbers Department Store I get asked the way to the Food Hall.

My other suit is THE TRENDY ONE. Or – to be more accurate – *was* THE TRENDY ONE. After a good lunch in the Kings Arms one day five years back I went out and bought this biscuit-coloured three-piece number with tight waist, bat-wing lapels wide enough for Concorde to land on and flaired trousers. Though it still manages to look cheap it has unfortu-nately proved to be very hardwearing. Louise says it makes me look like a footballer.

Obviously I need another one, but a suit seems SUCH A BORING THING TO SPEND MONEY ON. (I used not to think that. I used to think that *on me* it'd look like it did in the photograph, but self-knowledge and my paunch have en-croached too much for me to maintain that allusion.)

Louise thinks I ought to get another. She says I LET HER DOWN. But if I did decide to get another, what would I go for?

I couldn't afford the sort of hand-sculpted suit Grabber wears, which has to be transported from Saville Row to Knightsbridge by Securicore.

And I don't fancy Grint's light-weight American Prince-of-Wales cheque that strobes distressingly under the flourescent light when I get back from lunch.

Basil F-T's *reassuring* homespun tweeds aren't my style either.

Nor is Darryl Pacey's sharp little three-piece that makes him look like Steve Davis being interviewed after the match.

I suppose Peason has the nearest approach to mine when it comes to clothes – that they're not important and that they should be comfortable. But I do have some standards. I wouldn't go to work as he does looking like a lagged water-tank.

No, I think I'll wait till one of my two suits falls apart. Then I'll HAVE to do something.

I don't know though . . . I'll probably wait till the other one falls apart as well.

SHIRTS. A shirt is a shirt as far as I'm concerned and so long as you steer clear of the ones that change colour when you sweat there's not much more to say about them.

Some other people think they're more important.

Darryl Pacey actually has MONOGRAMS on his shirts (obviously some cheap Special Offer in one of the colour supplements). 'D.P.' it says over his nipple. I keep trying to come up with something offensive it could stand for, but though I know exactly the witheringly witty manner in which I would deliver the *bon meaux*, unfortunatley I can't think of anything. Did Oscar Wild have this trouble?

TIES. I tend to wear the O.C.T. (Old Custardian Tie) a lot.

This is not from reasons of loyalty/snobbery/Sir Henry Newbolt/5th Form at St Dominicks ect., just that it is an inoffensive object. In a discrete navy blue with a crimson motife of what is apparently a school prune on it, the O.C.T. is not the sort of tie to raise comment. It is pleasingly uncommunicative about me as a personality and St Cs was such a piddling little school there's not much danger of people recognising it.

(I wouldn't wear the Old Boy's Tie of my public school, Grunts, because you *do* ocasionally meet people who recognise that. 'Don't tell me you were at Grunts! Ha, ha. Did your parents know how they were being ripped off? Ha, ha, ha!' I'm not a charitable institution. I don't want to go through life giving people gratuitious belly-laughs.)

Grabber of course can wear his Old School Tie without fear of dirision. He also has a lot of silk ones with gold crests ect. all over them, mostly signifying membership of various exclusive regiments, peerages and clubs (incl. the US Club whose members, on recognising each other in the street, stand together and have a good sneer at THEM – i.e. US). All of Grabber's ties cost more each than I would spend on a suit (if I ever bought a suit).

Basil F-T's ties are home-woven. Most of them look as if they've just come off bales of hay, though a few reach the level of that webbing you get on the underside of chairs.

Peason's ties are quite revolting. Sharon buys them for him and she 'likes a bit of colour'. They do not harmonise with his suit (though that word is probably an offence under the Trades Description Act). But he is totally oblivious. (As usual. Peason maintains a more constant state of total oblivion than anyone I know. It's not just his post-coitial glaze; being an accountant has something to do with it. Like being a solicitor. Or in any of those other jobs where all you have to do is qualify and then sit back for the rest of your life and just watch the money come in.)

Darryl Pacey's ties are not discrete. Too bright, too patterned, and often worn with shirts whose patterns clash. This is indicitative of his background. (Hee-hee. Patrician snigger.)

UNDERWEAR. Things have got a bit friskier in this dept. since my St Cs school trunk had to contain:

> UNDERPANTS – 8 prs, cotton, white
>
> VESTS   – 4, sleeved, cotton, white

There has in fact been a major revolution.

Men's VESTS are now OUT, unless you call them T-SHIRTS or go the whole hog and have THERMAL ones. (THERMAL UNDERWEAR is now SEXY, implying not that you're an arthiritic old fossil, but that you're about to ski down the North Face of the Mattehorn, excevate the North Pole, ect., ect., ect.)

And men's UNDERPANTS can now be of any colour, shape or material you fancy. (Nor should you call them UNDERPANTS. BRIEFS, SHORTS or KNICKERS are in more general currancy.)

Mind you, the Underwear Revolution was not achieved without considerable opposition from the traditionalists. Denounciations of the new styles rang from pulpits all over the country . . . . *'For verily, brethren, ye underpante that is notte whyte is an abomination throughoute ye lande. For is it notte wrytten, Girde uppe your loines with purity, and whatte can be purer thanne whyte?*

'It is an heathen and backslydinge people that would wish to hyde their nether partes with all ye lassivious hues of ye rainbowe. For it is a flauntynge and unhealthy desyre to drawe attention to that which shoulde be concealed.

'Let us notte therefore, my people, harken to ye syren calle of noveltie. Let us notte even contemplate ye blacke underpante, ye redde, ye blue, ye purple, ye greene, ye puce, ye striped, ye gingam, ye paisly, ye Laura Asheley or ye polka dot! Let us shunne ye idolatrous underpantes of nylon, pollyester, tricelle, satinne, paper, leather, PVC, velvet or see-through pollythene! Lette us also be on our garde against ye underpantes that are printed with smuttie legendes – Pulle In Case Of Emergensie, Give Us A Hande, Now It's Uppe To You, or, This Is A Stick-Uppe! For alle these are abominations to true believers . . .' ect., ect., ect . . . .

But of course it all ended in the TRIUMPH OF PROGRESS, FREEDOM, PERMISSIVENESS, ECT., HURRAH HURRAH and now you're hard put to it to find a man with white underpants. (Well, actually I did notice when Basil Fotherington-Thomas forced me to play badminton that he . . . but then what would you expect?)

As a matter of fact Peason gave me a pair of briefs he had bought in Ampsterdam which had something printed on them which he said Sharon had found absolutely hysterical.

I haven't worn them, though.

I can't imagine Louise seeing the joke.

ACCESSARIES

SHOES. However carefully the young executive has chosen his wardrobe he can still be SERIOUSLY LET DOWN by his shoes.

Sneakers, brothelcreepers, trainers, cowboy boots, plimsoles, galoshes, espadrills, sandals, waders, slippersocks, clogs, wellingtons, glass slippers, ballet shoes, loafers, mules and pumps are thought to be inappropriate to the office (at least by Grint).

So, given this limitation on one's natural tastes, I think one can do a lot worse than a PLAIN BLACK SHOE, slip-on or lace-up.

And I mean PLAIN. People like Darryl Pacey wear sort of black moccasins with bits of horse-brasses or leather tassles on the front. I think these again just go to show that you can never make up the ground lost by not going to Public School. (Hee-hee, I may not have learnt much at Grunts but at least I'm a SNOB.)

BAGS. The reason men carry bags is not because they need them. The day's necessities (i.e. MONEY) can be carried in the pockets. But a brief-case makes a man LOOK AS IF HE HAS SOMETHING TO DO.

There are a variety of luggage styles available . . . .

Darryl Pacey of course has the full executive number, the kind of slim square black leather job imortalised in the James Bond films. His doesn't actually carry a machine-gun, capsule of nerve-gas and collapsable helicopter (at least I don't think it does), but it has most other refinements – combination locks, digital clock showing different time zones, calculater (as well no doubt as radiophone, computer terminal, telex, ect., ect., ect.). Its interior is always unbelievably neat, pens and pencils in their alotted straps, papers alligned to .000000000000 0000000001 millimeters. It's not my idea of a case. For one thing, IT HAS NEVER HAD A SANDWICH PUT IN IT.

Basil Fotherington-Thomas carries his solicitor's equipment (contracts, deeds, willforms ('Have you made a will yet, Nigel?'), bills and all the other bits designed to CONFUSE

THE CLIENT, which is what being a solicitor is ABOUT) in a LEATHER SHOULDER-BAG.

This is part of the Fotherington-Thomas Scheme to PRE-TEND THAT HE ISN'T A SOLICITOR and lull his clients into a false sense of security (until his bill arrives and further pretence is impossible).

This is symtomatic of the way he lives the rest of his life, PRETENDING HE ISN'T WHAT HE IS, viz.:

1 He and Araminta live in the suburbs but decorate their house to PRETEND they live in the country.
2 They are very rich (he is a solicitor QED), but PRETEND to live like peasants (all those quishes and all that weaving).
3 They buy expensive raw materials for corn dollies, macramee, wine, ect., but PRETEND they are independent of the commercial world.
4 They are anti-pollution, but drive a Citreon 2CV, which they PRETEND is not a car.
5 They watch Channel Four, which they PRETEND is not the same as watching television.
6 They vote SDP, which they PRETEND is the same as not having any politics . . . .

Actually, they may have a point on the last two.
Sorry. Getting away from BAGS.
But you know what I mean.

My apalling brother Steve carries a HANDBAG.

This is not something I wish to discuss. It will only get me going on the rest of his wardrobe and then I start sounding like a retired Colonel on 'Any Answers'.

Steve says a handbag's perfectly normal in the pop world, but I don't reckon anything's normal in the pop world so let's move on.

Peason is an accountant, as you know, and he is a slob, as you also know. But he was a slob before he was an accountant and so he carries things to work in a GRABBO SUPERMARKET PLASTIC CARRIER BAG.

And I? What of I? What does the sauve sophisticate around GBH use as hand luggage?

Hem-hem. I have to confess I still lug around the leather briefcase I had at St Cs.

I love its familiar worn contours, its shiny patches of congealed bubblegum, ink blotches, homely grafiti ('GILLI-BRAND IS A WET', 'THE MEKON FOR EVER', ect.) and unraveling seams. Call me sentimental old fool if you will, but every inch of that scarred leather is history for me. It is my past in portmanteaue form.

Grint does not like my case. He has more than once expressed that this is not the image he invisages for the Invoice Docketting (Internal) Department.

Louise does not like my case either. It is not the image she invisages for her husband (but then *I'm* not the image she invisages for her husband, we know *that*).

But *I* like it. I think it has CLASS. And I'm going to keep it.

WALLETS, ECT. Everyone has to carry MONEY (even Basil F-T, who PRETENDS he is above such material considerations).

And everyone knows that men who use purses are either:

a) perverts,
b) mean,
c) characters in television situation comedies, or,
d) peculiar in some other way.

(Basil does use a purse incidentally which just goes to prove my point.)

So the rest of us are stuck with WALLETS.

Here again there is a variety available . . . .

Mine is much on the lines of my bag – i.e. ancient and battered. It is a long one which when worn in the inside pocket of my jacket digs into my armpit, but it is of such old soft leather that this doesn't matter. (Louise once gave me a swish new green leather one with brass corners. After one day I had to give up using it because of lasserated armpits.)

My wallet, like my bag, is full of memories. Ah, what secrets has it from time to time not held? The history of my love-life BL (Before Louise) was between those leathern folds. Optimistic photographs, more optimistic phone numbers, *extremely* optimistic contraceptives. (Well opportunities were supposed to arise all the time in the Swinging Sixties. The fact that they never did is neither here nor there.)

The only person I know who doesn't carry his money in a wallet or purse is my apalling brother Steve. He just has a roll of loose notes, from which he peels off fivers with infuriating nonchalence.

I like to think that there are only fivers on the outside and that the middle of the roll is blank paper, but I have a horrible feeling THIS IS NOT TRUE.

Darryl Pacey's wallet is one of the green leather with brass corners numbers that Louise tried to impale me on.

Inside it is like NAASA Control at Houston. It contains a paperthin calculator which works out pension differentials and plays Mendelson on Darrylandcarryl's Wedding Anniversary. It also bleeps at various preset times (moments by which Darryl reckons he should have climbed another rung of the management ladder). In fact he has a lot of things about his person that bleep – his watch, his brief-case, his pen, his desk-tidy, ect. It's like sharing an office with a Space Invader.

But the most striking thing about Darryl's wallet is its Credit Card Holder. This is a string of transparent pockets which all fold together and unravell like a concertina. Fully extended, Darryl's reaches across our office and right the way over the corridor into the Invoice Docketting (External).

A Digression on Credit Cards

The use and management of credit cards is another of those executive accomplishements which I do not posess.

I hold a humble ACCESS one with a credit limit I won't embarass you by mentioning and I do get JOLLY SICK of Darryl Pacey constantly saying, 'Of course credit cards are very costeffective if you pay off the full amount as soon as the bill comes in, blah blah blah.' Needless to say, I, like every other right-minded person, pay the absolute minimum as late as possible and get lumbered with all that 'excessive interest' Darryl keeps going on about.

Grabber, needless to say, pays for EVERYTHING with his

American Express Platinum Card, which grants the holder a trillion pound overdraught, unlimited supplies of free champagne and *droit de seignuer* over every woman he meets.

LEISUREWEAR

There used not to be LEISUREWEAR, chiefly because there used not to be LEISURE. There used to be BEING AT WORK and DOING NOTHING, without anything in between. I think there was a lot to be said for that. Now one is under constant pressure to PARTICIPATE in leisure and, of course, to wear the apropriate wardrobe.

All Leisurewear is based on Sports Kit.

The idea of it is that you get everyone walking around looking like international atheletes. Middleaged men put on satin shorts, singlets and track-suits to drive down to the pub. Sweatsuits are worn by ladies far to elegant ever to have sweated in their lives. People who can barely totter from the Salloon to the Public Bar wear training shoes. The isles of the Grabbo Supermarket on a Saturday look like backstage at the Olympics.

One of the nastiest experienses of my life – worse even (if you can beleive this) than the first time I heard Molesworth ii playing Fairy Bells on the St Cs school piano – was meeting Darrylandcarryl one afternoon on Wimbledon Common. Bad enough under any circs, but made much worse by the fact that they were dressed in identical grey and red Guiness jogging-suits.

YERK. That kind of shock could prove fatal to someone at my delicate stage of life. I swear I got a pain in the chestal area.

I hope I have made it clear that I WILL NEVER BE SEEN DEAD IN ANYTHING THAT COMES UNDER THE HEADING OF 'LEISUREWEAR'.

(Actually I probably will because when I'm dead there will be no one to curb Louise's image of what I should be like. I'll be the only corpse in the mortuary in a Guiness jogging-suit.)

You see, Louise thinks I'd look rather good in that sort of thing. That's what the Ideal Nigel Molesworth of Her Dreams (a.k.a. Rennaisance Man) would wear while finishing his oil painting of her, humming a snatch of opera and planning his next novel.

This makes life difficult. I have to get up early on Sunday mornings and rip all the Mail Order Leisurewear Special Offers out of the Colour Supplements before Louise secs them.

THE NIGEL MOLESWORTH COLLECTION

Back at St Cs I once had this ghastly daydream of what the future held for me and my Crystal Ball showed an image of Nigel Molesworth, FASHION DESIGNER.

ERG. What a ghastly idea, I thought at the time. Imagine spending your life being a trendsetter, making lots of money and being surrounded by beautiful models all the time – how awful.

Well, I have changed my attitudes a bit since then and now I must say I wouldn't mind it. Apparently it's a well-known fact (or at least Peason says) that since nearly all fashion designers are gay, all these beautiful models are TERRIBLY FRUSTRATED and if you happen to be a straight one you virtually have to FIGHT THEM OFF. And I feel that's the kind of situation I could, in time, learn to live with.

But I have to be realistic. To start being a fashion designer in my late thirties would be difficult and experience in the GBH Invoice Docketting (Internal) Department is not going to have much direct relevence.

Still, I can dream.

AND I DO. That's what's strange about it. I must have had the Fashion Designer Daydream at a very impressionable age, because it has now joined my repetoire of RECURRANT DREAMS (along with Helping The Queen Down From A Hazardrous Mountain, Running A Mile In Three Minutes At The Olympics, Dismembering Grint With A Chainsaw, and some others too personel to divulge).

What happens every time is that all the fashion experts of the world have gathered in my *sallon* for THE NIGEL MOLESWORTH COLLECTION.

A hushed voice takes over the commentry . . . .

'And the usual glittering assembly is here for the fashion event of the year. What surprises has Nigel up his sleeve this time?

Or will he make the sleeve go the way of the crinaline and the doublet and hose?

'With what breathless antisipation we await the entry of the first model. The main lights dim, the spotlights come on, the music surges – oh, and the show begins!

'*Et viola* – the first model comes down the catwalk. Her name is FELICITIAH GRABBER and she is dressed in a stunning creation in wild silk.

'Countless African bushmen gave their lives in the hunt for this silk, which was then woven by Atzec craftsmen on Gautemalan looms, died by Scottish lairds in vintage port, malt whiskey, liquid gold, ect., ect., conceptualised by Taki of Hollywood, executed by Abelard and Elouise of Paris and bought for Mrs Grabber by her husband's Little Man Who Buys Presents For His Wife for a mere three trillion pounds.

'What a picture Mrs Grabber looks! Her jewellry is by courtesy of Tutankamun, her shoes by Kurt Gucchi of Rome, her handbag by Ukibuki of Tokio, her hair by Nancio Puffi of Athens, and her sneer by force of habit . . . .

'Now the music changes to a pounding rock and roll rythm. And bobbing into the spotlight comes an adolescent fantasy – sweater tight over breasts that look as if they've been in a pencil-sharpener, waist clinched in a waspie belt, skirt forced out by a froth of petticoats, shapely legs tapering down to flourescent socks . . . .

'Yes, it's the lovely SHARON PEASON, doing her Fifties number. A vision of delight – or she would be but for the shambling figure that accompanies her, ungainly on crape soles, paunch wobbling over the top of drainpipes, long jacket and bootlace tie flying in his pathetic attempt to dance, hair in greasy quiff and face even now bearing a remarkable resemblence to a squished tomatoe.

'And once again the question on everyone's lips is : WHAT DOES SHE SEE IN HIM? . . . .

'But what are these two manure-coloured sacks entering the *sallon*? Can it be that someone has misdirected a load of hampster fodder?

'No, *au cointreau*. It is ARAMINTA and ARRABELLA FOTHERINGTON-THOMAS, dressed in the fruits of their own loom. Yes, what looks like the emptyings of an overloaded

Hoover is in fact fabric which they have WOVEN THEMSELVES.

'Pains-taking gathering of dog's hairs from the barbed wire of Wimbledon Common went to make the yarn of these unique garments. An authentic Cumbrian twiddler's poke was used to turn the hairs into thread. That thread was then died by Thoby and Ghislane in ways we needn't go into, and woven by today's models on authentic Welsh spindle-picker's sprocket-looms.

'And the result is this *eau natural* look – a romantic haze of manure-coloured fuzz.

'ERG. Just to look at it makes you want to start scratching . . . .

'And now a vision in washable, drip-dry, crumple-proof mail-order elegence! My, the crisp outlines of that ruffled blouze! Oh, the sharp lines of that air-hostess two-piece! Ah, the sparkle of costume jewellry! Ooh, the *sheen* of the tights, the *gleam* of the patent leather shoes! Not a hair out of place! Not a crease to be seen!

'But who can it be, this parragon giving Cindy-doll impersonations?

'It is of course CAROLE PACEY, the perfect executive accessary. (AVAILABLE IN NAVY BLUE, BURGUNDY, OATMEAL, GOOSEBERRY OR MANGOLIA. ALLOW UP TO FOUR WEEKS FOR DELIVERY. ALL MAJOR CREDIT CARDS ACCEPTED.)

'But who have we here? Can such a tiny piece of fabric be termed a skirt? What save willpower can be holding up that diaphonous blouze? Surely no one has as much thigh as that . . . . Or so deep a cleavidge . . . .

'Yes, it is CHARLEEN . . . .

Actualy round this point I usually find the nature of my dream changes and the Nigel Molesworth Collection is crowded off the screen of my mind by MORE RAMPANT IMAGES.

7

CHILDREN

Or, He Needs Changing – Yes,
Preferably for a Mercedes

Children give a whole new dimention to life. So everyone says and they may have a point. Certainly the thought of ones genes being pepertuated in the form of new human beings is quite soberring. (The thought of ones wifes relation's genes also being pepertuated is even more soberring.)

I mean gosh, the magic of new life, the eternal miracle of childbirth, the wonder of creation, ect., ect., ect. (If you want more in this vain – and have got about 3 wks to spare – get Basil and Araminta Fotherington-Thomas onto the subj.)

Against this amazing life-inhancing aspect of it all must be weighed the fact that MOST CHILDREN ARE RIGHT LITTLE PAINS.

And, objective chronicler to the last, I would include my own offspring in this assesment. (In fact I would put them high on the list.)

I have two. (Well, so has Louise. The same two actualy.) They are called Tristram and Lucinda. (I had nothing to do with the names. Louise chose them IPROMISEIPRO-MISEIPROMISE.).

It was also Louise who decided to have them. When we discussed the – no, get it right, when she told me about this decision, I argued that they could only proove disruptive to our domestic harmony.* I ennumerated their disadvantages – economic, social, hygenic, environemental, ect., ect., ect. I was quite elloquent.

Then Louise told me she was pregnant anyway.

That was Tristram, now 11, who combines all the reppelence

* I was right – Ed.

of Louise's side of the family with none of my own natural sauveness, *savoie-fair*, wit, good looks, ect.

Underterred by this ghastly warning, 3 yrs later Louise announced we were going to have Lucinda, now aged 8, who is like Tristram only wetter.

(Let it not be thought, gentle reader, that I am totaly lacking in natural affection. My children are ocasionally charming and manys the time their quaint antics have brought a throb to my throat and a tear to my manly bosom. But the fact remains that, viewed objectivley, most of the time they are RIGHT LITTLE PAINS.)

One of the big disadvantages of having a child in the house is that other children gravitate towards it. Your own may seem bad enough, but seeing other peoples can make you feel quite priveliged by comparison.

Though I have done my best to avoid it, I have had to meet quite a few children in the last 11 years, and I have learnt to recognise the main types and their individual forms of reppelence.

THUGS. These are children who have only to see another child to start thumping it up. I do not approove of this. I think that sort of thing comes better from an ADULT (preferably me).

Parents of Thugs have a difficult time, because after a few experienses of mopping up blood, tears ect., going to Hospital Casuality Depts, picking up broken teeth, limbs ect., other parents stop inviting their offspring round.

Most Thugs parents get round this by giving lots of parties. They know that the lure of Pass-the-Parcel and Going-Home Presents will always proove too strong and they also know one of the inilluctable rules of Bringing Up Children: YOU MUST INVITE TO YOUR CHILD'S PARTY ANY CHILD TO WHO'S PARTY YOUR CHILD HAS BEEN INVITED.

In this way they insure a ready supply of victims for their child to beat up.

TANKS. Tanks have much the same affect as Thugs (q.c.), but do not do it on purpose. They are sturdey little people (usually, but by no means always, boys) who leave a trail of devestation wherever they go.

They knock over any piece of furniture that is not actualy nailed to the ground and clear any surface of ornements in 0.0000000000000000000000000001 secs flat. They are magneticly drawn towards anything breakable (and this goes for people as well as objects).

There parents tend to laugh it all off saying things like, 'There's my brave little soldier, He's all boy, She doesnt know her own strenghth' ect. This does not help the victims at all.

I do not know how to stop a tank. (THINKS: A hand-grenade is the traditional way. Maybe I should try it.)

SISSIES. Sissies cry at everything and spend all their time clinging to the backs of their mothers legs. Their parents use words like 'shy' and 'sensitive' to describe them, but I have a few others.

Sissies are very boring and never want to do anything that is suggested. They also cry if I look at them, which I find odd (thought Timothy Peason says its hardly surprising).

If a Sissie comes round to our house, my usual course of action is to find the nearest Thug (q.c.) and set it on it.

I feel this is a generous act which teaches the Sissie to undestand the difference between the Actual World and the World of Imagination – i.e. it gives it something REAL to cry about.

PRISSIES. These are the worst of the lot. They are self-rightious little prigs of both sexes who constantly make one aware of their rightiousness.

E.g. When given prunes for lunch, a Prissie will say, 'I do not actualy like prunes, but I am nevertheless going to eat them up without any fuss.'

Or, when another child pulls its hair (a perfectly reasonable thing to do, given the provocation), a Prissie will say, 'I'm not going to tell my Mummy that you pulled my hair,' just loud enough for its Mummy to hear.

Whenever I encounter a Prissie, I find I want to HIT IT EXTREMLEY HARD (though if I did it'd probably say, 'I'm not going to tell my Mummy that you hit me,' at exactly the right level, and then the Mummy'd come and thump me up).

PRODIDGIES. These are children of enormous intellegence who make adults feel inadaquate.

When playing with its Leggo a Prodidgy will make a model of a molicule that has never been discovered before.

When playing with its Action Man, a Prodidgy will produce a brand-new theory of why Rommel lost the Dessert War.

At bedtime a Prodidgy will sit its parents down and read Proust to them.

Neither Tristram nor Lucinda is a Prodidgy thank goodness. I already have sufficcient difficulty answerring their questions. What it must be like if youve got a genius to cope with I cant imagine.

Well, I can actualy . . . .

(The scene is a nursury. A father tucks his tiny tot up in its tiny cot.)

FATHER   Night, night, my little poppet.

TOT   Do you use 'poppet' in the sense of a cyllindrical case for pins and needles, an upright piece of a turning-lath, or one of the protuberences on the gunnel of a boat supporting the wash-strake and forming the rollox?

FATHER   Um . . . er . . . I've no idea.

TOT   Are you using the word 'idea' in the Platonnic sense?

FATHER   I dont know. You tell me.

TOT   Well, acording to Plato, the 'idea' is the ideal form of an object, and individual objects partake of the nature of this ideal. Thus an individual Teddy Bear could be said to partake of the nature of an 'idea' of a Teddy Bear. The 'idea' of a Teddy Bear is *real* and the Teddy Bear that you see is only *apparent*. Do I make myself clear?

FATHER   Strewth, cor blimey . . . .

TOT   May I reccomend for your perusual *Wittgenkant's Philosophicle Conceptualizations* (pub. Grabber & Grabber @ £75) in which certain of the basics are spelled out in a way that even a bonehead like you would undestand. Then perhaps you should read . . . ect., ect., ect.

I THINK THERES QUITE A LOT TO BE SAID FOR HAVING DIM CHILDREN.

DODGES FOR AVOIDING CHILDREN

The obvious way to get round the problem is not to have any, but for many of us it's too late for such delisious fantesies. So, given the existance of the little pains, the parent has to devise ways of seeing them as little as possible.

The main trouble with children is that they are ALWAYS THERE.

Tristram and Lucinda wander round our house as if they lived there, leaving a permanent trail of contorted Cindies and Action Men. Its a bit much.

I cannot even for a moment pretend they do not exist (and God knows I've tried). I have only to sit down in front of the television for one of them to come up and interupt me with a fatuous question like why is the grass green, or if Gods everywhere is he in our vests, or how does electricity work.

Even when their tiny curley heads are on the pillow I cant forget them. Every armchair I sit in attacks my buttocks with lumps of Leggo. Every wall I look at has on it some awful colage of silver foil, lentels, eggboxes and finger-painting. Every pair of socks I get out of my draw comprises one of mine and one six inches shorter.

Since it is impossible to be unaware of ones children in ones own house, the only solution is to GO OUT AS MUCH AS POSSIBLE.

Some fathers do this by always being at work, flying off on business trips ect. This is quite a good wheeze, because then on the two ocasions a year when you do go home you get a heros welcome.

You are introduced to your charmingly unfamilier offspring and give them lavish presents before buzzing off again. They come to think of you as some kind of *dais ex macina,* a Father Christmas or Lone Ranger figure, which improves the father-child relationship no end (and which doesn't do any harm to the husband-wife relationship).

Wheras if your the sort of father like me who comes home every day you just become a demonstration for your children of that old adage that FAMILIARITTY BREEDS CONTEMPT.

(The only disadavantage of the being-away-a-lot wheeze is

that you do actualy have to do rather a lot of WORK. I find the basic 10–6 day at GBH, even with three hours out for lunch, is already too much, so this method is unfortunatley not for me.)

Another approach is not to remove yourself from the source of irittation, but to remove the irittant itself – i.e. get rid of them.

Unfortunatley the days when you could get a few bob for your children from chimney-sweeps or have them sent down the mines to detect poisenous gasses are gone, so all you're really left with are boarding schools.

And these have got distressingly lenient since my young day. No longer the savage incarserration I sufferred at St Cs and Grunts; now the young gentlemen seem allowed to come and go mororless at will, and their parents see almost as much of them as if they were living at home. Which destroys the whole point of the exercice.

When I was thinking about Tristram's education I tried to find a brochure for Dootheboys Hall or somewhere else that doesnt have holidays, but all of those estimable establishements seem to have gone out of business.

So the parent who decides on boarding school has to set up a whole new lot of schools for the holidays – sailing schools, pony-trecking schools, clarinet schools, Bible-reading schools, potholing schools – in fact anything that'll keep the children out of the house.

But the trouble is THIS IS V. EXPENSIVE. In fact, money is the drawback to the whole wheeze. I know that my parents put two of us through boarding prep. and public school, but I cannot imagine how they managed it. (Perhaps my apalling brother Steve's suspisions were correct and the Old Man did do a bit of gun-running on the side.)

Anyway, for someone on CJ2/B level in Invoice Docketting at GBH, sending 2 kids to boarding school is out of the q.

It's not just the basic fees that are so apalling – though theyre bad enough – its all the extras. And those have got a lot worse SINCE EDUCATION HAS GOT MORE LIBERATED. The bills nowadays look frightful . . . .

ST MARIJUANA'S ACADEMY

Summer Solstice Term – Invoice

(NB – Early settlement can let you off a lot of very uncool hassles.)

TUTION FEES	£ 500.00
ACOMMODDATION FEES	£1000.00
Suana (EXTRA)	£ 100.00
Jackuzi (EXTRA)	£ 150.00
EQUIPMENT – Basic	£ 150.00
Cricket – Helmet (EXTRA)	£ 50.00
Music – Personal Stereo (EXTRA)	£ 100.00
Politics – Riot Sheild (EXTRA)	£ 50.00
– Plastic Explosives (EXTRA)	£ 200.00
Sex Education – To Services of Miss Fifi and Miss Whiplashe (EXTRA)	£ 250.00
BUTTERY – Alcohol – Basic	£ 50.00
Alcohol (EXTRA)	£ 500.00
SCHOOL BARBER -- Basic Haircuts	£ 15.00
– Dying, highlights, perms, ect. (EXTRA)	£ 150.00
Was-there-anything-else-sir (EXTRA)	£ 50.00
STATIONARY COSTS – Basic	£ 50.00
Glue (for sniffing) (EXTRA)	£ 100.00
SUBTOTAL	£3465.00
SERVICE @ 12½%	£ 433.12
VAT @ 15%	£ 519.75
TOTAL	£4417.87

(DO NOT ASK FOR CREDIT AS REFUSAL MAY OFFEND.)

Another way of keeping children out of their parents way is to get in STAFF.

Trim NANNIES in grey or blue uniforms do, I am assured, still exist outside erotic fantesies and there are still parents who employ them as part of a conspiracy to pretend their children are Christopher Robin.

Needless to say, Felicitiah Grabber has about a trillion Nannies to handle her children, rather in the way scientists have those sleeve things with pincers on the end to handle toxic waste.

THERE ARE TWO SORTS OF NANNIES:

OLD-STYLE Nannies produce little boys in tweed jackets with velvet collers, little girls in smocked dresses, and little homalies on keeping regular.

NEW-STYLE Nannies are very laid-back. They produce children in unisex dungerees and teach them to be very laid-back too. They are amazingly expensive – even more expensive than Old-Style Nannies. That, in fact, as with boarding schools, is the BIG SNAG with Nannies – THE COST. I like the idea of my children being presented to me once a day for inspection like fresh clean loaves of bread baked by a Nanny who does all the boring bits, but I know I could never afford it. (Another example of the wicked inequalitties of modern life – ONLY THE RICH CAN AFFORD TO HAVE THEIR CHILDREN KEPT OUT OF THEIR SIGHT.)

Some people who cant afford Nannies think they may be able to get the same sort of service cheaper from AU PERE GIRLS. They are wrong.

Au Pere Girls, like Nannies, spend a lot of time drifting diaphonously through other peoples erotic fantesies. But that is in the Ideal World; none of the Au Pere Girls I've met in the Real World would pass the audition into one of my erotic fantesies.

They were all built like prop forwards and turned out to be either homesick, anorexic, criminal, allergic to children, or Belgian. Their massed sex apeal was slightly less than that of a frozen cod stake in batter.

And having watched families who have had Au Pere Girls, I can confidantly say that they cause more work than they save and for the hard-pressed parents it's just like having more children (but foriegn ones) in the house.

My researches show that NO ONE EVER HAS A HAPPY EXPERIENSE WITH AN AU PERE GIRL. (Except for my apalling brother Steve once in Swiss Cottage but we neednt go into that.)

ACTUALY, it doesnt do to be too nasty about your children, because there is always the chance you may need them to LOOK AFTER YOU IN YOUR OLD AGE. So the ocasional smile, word of encouragement, pkt. of friut gums ect. may well prove to be an investment.

I sometimes vizualise my last hours, attended by my greif-stricken offspring. (I'm prepared to conceed that a few of the minor details of the following scene may be a little exagerated.)

(It is the great bedchamber of Molesworth Manor. The walls are hung with portrates, citations, honourary doctorites, ect. In the great bed, their subject, Earl Molesworth of Albion, whitebearded and venerable, aged 107, lies breathing heavily. His children, Tristram and Lucinda, along with those of the second marriage, cluster sobbing by the bed. [His first wife, Louise, has long since passed on. It was after her demese that the Earl's love match and subseqent marriage to the Princess of Wales caused one of the most famous royal divorce scandels in history.] A heavenley choir sings somewhere.)

EARL M   *(in a voice as soft as thissledown)* I am fading
              fast . . . .

LUCINDA   No, no, I cannot bare it! *(rennewed sobbing)*

EARL M   It has to be. To everything there is a season
              and this is mine. *(even more thissledowny)* It
              is time for me to waft away, vannish as if I
              had never been, time for the world to forget
              me . . . .

TRISTRAM   But you will never be forgotten, Father. You
              leave so much. The 150 novels. The 700
              plays. The 80 Liesure Centres. All
              aknowledged masterpieces.

EARL M   Soon faded. Sucess is a fickle misstress.

LUCINDA   But your political acheavements will not be
              forgotten so easily. The finest Foreign Sec of
              the century, special envoy to the White House.

EARL M	*(wryley)* Ha. What are titles? Mere toys. No, the only honour that I value is the Nobel prize.
TRISTRAM	Which one?
EARL M	Peace. Litterature and Science are such commercial dissiplines. And now –
LUCINDA	Oh, Father . . . . *(renewed sobbing)*
EARL M	Now I will slip away like the breeze of a summer morning . . . Goodbye . . . Goodbye . . . .
TRISTRAM	*(unable to contain his sobs)* Oh, Father . . . .
EARL M	Goooooooodbyyyyyyyye . . . . . *(dies)*
TRISTRAM	He is gone. *(Lucinda and the other children are overcome with emotion.)* Who can ever try to fill that void? For we that remain nothing can ever be the same. By comparrison with his great acheavements all else must be forever secondrate. *(He closes the old man's eyes.)* Now there is much to do. First I must ring *The Times* – tell them to hold the centre-spread for his obittuary! ect., ect., ect.

I DONT KNOW – MAYBE IT WONT BE EXACTLY LIKE THAT . . . .

Some people reckon children get better as they get older and there may be something in this. The theory is that their reppelence diminishes as they become more like adults. The only trouble with this is that in my view most adults are pretty reppelent too, so the gain is likely to be small.

There are however some advantages of children growing up but these tend to be purely practical – e.g. they do not need nappies any more, they can learn to tie their own shoelaces, ties, ect., ect., ect. The trouble is that looming ahead of every parent is the prospect of PUBERTEY. I think as soon as Tristram and Lucinda demonstrate any symtoms of this, I will retire into a monastry for a few years. I know that I – even I, Nigel Molesworth – was pretty revolting during Pubertey and I cannot think that my poor children, without my natural advantages, will be any less so.

No, when I come down to it, the only real bennefit I can see of children growing up is that they learn to read for themselves and their poor parents no longer have to read THE SORT OF RUBBISH THAT PASSES THESE DAYS FOR CHILDREN'S BOOKS. You know the kind of thing I mean . . . .

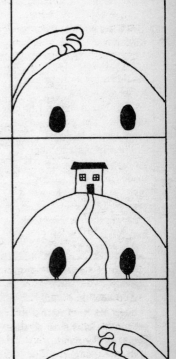

Mr Rich had always wanted to be rich. From a very early age he had thought to himself, 'Oh, how I'd like to be rich!'

But there was a problem. He hadn't got any money.

And it's very difficult to be rich when you haven't got any money.

Poor Mr Rich!

Mr Rich lived in Poorland, where all the people were poor.

But he wanted to move to Richland, where all the people were rich.

How was he going to do it?

That was the problem.

'What I need,' thought Mr Rich, 'is an IDEA.'

'It must be a very simple IDEA, because I'm a very simple sort of person.'

So Mr Rich put on his thinking-cap and tried to think up an IDEA.

He thought and he thought and he thought.

Then one day an IDEA came to him. Just like that!

'I know,' he thought. 'I will write a series of children's books!'

That was quite a good IDEA, but then Mr Rich had an even better IDEA.

'And,' he thought, 'I will make them all EXACTLY THE SAME!'

What a good IDEA that was!

So that very afternoon, he sat down for an hour and wrote six books.

'Ten minutes each,' he thought. 'I'm sure I can do them faster than that.'

Then he added some pictures to the books. He made them very simple pictures, because he was a very simple sort of person.

Doing the pictures took him ALL THE REST OF THE AFTERNOON!

Then he started to sell his books.

And how they sold!

Soon Mr Rich started to get much richer than all the people in Poorland.

But he thought, 'Why should I stop at books? I'm sure there are lots of other things I can sell!'

And that was his second good IDEA!

So he started to take the little people out of his books and put them onto other things.

He put them onto Tea-shirts, writing paper, soap, waste-paper-baskets, sticking-plasters, sweets, lollys, bisciuts, toothbrushes, pencils, kites and deoderants.

What a lot of things Mr Rich put his little people on!

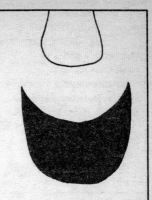

And Mr Rich's second IDEA worked!

Everything with his little people on just SOLD and SOLD.

And Mr Rich moved out of Poorland.

And he moved to Richland.

And, do you know, he's still there.

Getting RICHER and RICHER!

Well done, Mr Rich!

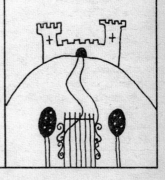

8

SPORT

*Or, And England Seem to be in
All Kinds of Trouble*

One thing I remember thinking when I left my public school, Grunts (and lets face it, there werent many – it wasnt an institution to encourage such effeet self-indulgence as thought) was AT LEAST I WILL NEVER HAVE TO PLAY ANY FORM OF SPORT EVER AGAIN IN MY LIFE.

The implications of this thought reverbarated through my body, and promted the following drama in its Defense Mechanism:

(Scene: A ~~beleagured belegaured bealaugaured bal~~ hard-pressed outpost of the Molesworth lymph glands. A small group of antebodies gather in a dugout. One of them plays 'Lily Marleen' on a harmonica.)

1ST ANTEBODY	I dont like it. It's too quiet. What are those germs up to out there?
2ND ANTEBODY	*(one of those perrenially cheerful cockney types beloved of british filmmakers in the forties)* Don't worry, Sarge. We'll be all right. Just so long as Nigel keeps looking after himself.
1ST ANTEBODY	But will he do that, Chalky? We're already fully stretched by the number of cigs he manages to consume after Lights Out. And dont forget that Emergency Mission we had to make to the Liver after he got hold of Matron's gin.

2ND ANTEBODY	You're taking it all too seriously, Sarge. Everyone gets morbid when they've been at the front line as long as you have. You need a break.
1ST ANTEBODY	I know I do, Chalky. Just to get back to normality – ah, what wouldnt I give for that? *(suddenly quiet)* I dream of being with Valerie and the kids, you know, in our little house in East Spleen . . . But . . . . *(he pauses)* War is hell, Chalky.
2ND ANTEBODY	Yes, Sarge. But dont worry. Its all for the best. So long as Nigel keeps taking regular exercice and –
1ST ANTEBODY	*(looking out over the lymphatic cappilaries)* Oh my God, look! It's Lofty! They're absolutely bombarding him with bacteriaea! He'll never make it! *(3rd antebody staggers into the dugout, more dead than alive.)* Lofty . . . .
3RD ANTEBODY	*(very feebley)* Don't go in there guv. Its 'orrible, 'orrible. I thilnk I've bought it, Sarge, but I had to get here to tell you . . . . *(he gasps)*
1ST ANTEBODY	Yes, Lofty, what is it?
3RD ANTEBODY	It's him – Nigel Molesworth – he's decided . . . . *(he gasps even more feebley)*
1ST ANTEBODY	Yes?
3RD ANTEBODY	HE'S NEVER GOING TO PLAY ANY FORM OF SPORT EVER AGAIN IN HIS LIFE!
1ST ANTEBODY	OH MY GOD!!!
3RD ANTEBODY	*(for whom the effort has prooved too much)* Erg . . . Tell Laura I love her . . . Erg . . . . *(dies)*
1ST ANTEBODY	Lofty . . . Poor, poor Lofty . . . He's dead.
2ND ANTEBODY	Oh, yes, but you've got to look on the bright –

VOICE OF GERM HAUPTGRUPPPE-NFUHRER	(off, calling through loudhaler) All richt, Tommies. Ve hav heard ze newz. Your cause iz hopeless. Zurender now und zave yourzelf a lot of trouble!
IST ANTEBODY	NEVER!!!
VOICE OF GERM HAUPTGRUPPPE-NFUHRER	(off) All richt, you hav for it asked! (Calling orders through loudhaler) Richt, men, bring up Obeesity! Get ze Cihrrosis Squad down to ze Liver! Mobilize ze Cororonary Sturmtroopers!, ect., ect., ect.
IST ANTEBODY	This is it, Chalky! The end!
2ND ANTEBODY	Dont you believe it, Sarge. Everything's going to be all right. Every cloud has a silver –
IST ANTEBODY	OH, SHUT UP, YOU SILLY LITTLE MAN!!! (He shoots 2nd antebody and rushes out to face the enemy on his own in a quicksottic gesture of defiance.)

So you see, with almost touching näivitee I thought that, once I had escaped the suffocating bosoms of my *almer maters*, St Custards and Grunts, and the odious blandishments of demented beaks on the touchline in exessive efforts for the honour of the house (COMEONYOUCANDOBETTER-THANTHATMOLESWORTH!!! REMEMBERTHEBIG-GERTHEYARETHEHARDERTHEYFALL!!!), I would be free in pepertuity from people trying to make me play sport.

NOT A BIT OF IT.

In fact, I think it gets worse as I get increasingly seer and yellow.

Its no longer only the pathetic flotsom and jetsom of the academic world who try to force me into uncongenial exercice – everyone now seems to have taken over the roll of the beaks. They're all dedicated to preventing the graceful decline into innertia, which is the future that from an early age I promised to my body. Wives, doctors, television gurus, books, cornflake packets, car stickers and Jimmy Saville all urge me to get out there and DO SOMETHING.

And – alas! – I do not always have the strength of will to resist all this promting. Quite honestly its sometimes less sweat just to get out there than to have them all nagging all the time.

Any way, let me give you a quick rundown on a few major SPORTS and my attitude to them.

JOGGING is, thank goodness, becoming less fashionable. There was a time a few years back when there was severe media pressure to participate in it.

Round about that time Louise bought *The Joy Of Jogging* (pub. Grabber & Grabber @ £7.95) and seemed all set to start (i.e. bought three track suits and matching running shoes).

And I – even I, Nigel Molesworth – was forced to lollop out round the leafy purlieues of Wimbledon.

Now fortunatley sufficcient people have died of heart attacks ect. for Louise to stop going on at me about it. (The ultimate secret weapon to get out of doing anything for Louise is to say its a threat to my heart. The mention of pain in the chestal area always stops her short and will continue to do so until I take out a trillion-pound insurance policy. Worth bearing in mind.)

But at the height of the jogging craze the pressure was ferocious. Louise came in when I'd just got out of the bath one morning and looked at my body with ill-disguised disgust.

'You should get yourself in shape,' she announced.

'I am in shape,' I quipped back, quick as a flash. 'Pear-shape.'

But Wildian shafts of wit were not enough to deterr her. She nagged away until I felt forced to don antequated shorts, tea-shirt and plimsolls and face the chill early-morning humours of Wimbledon.

I started off down Arbutus Ave and felt the suprising pleasure of the rippling power of my own body. Exilaration flared in my vanes as nerve gave message to mussel, mussel to bone, leg to foot ect. (I can go on writing like this for some time you know.)

As my body's presision machinery started to pump out its power, I seemed to hear a new voice in my ear. It was David Coleman or Ron Pickerring (or both).

And this boy really is one of the discoveries of the season! Yes, Molesworth has really put a new complection on British prospects for the Marathon. And what a fairy-tale story his is! Unregarded as a club athlete, his most

recent timed performance before this year an unconfirmed 58.7 seconds for
the Egg and Spoon Race at St Custards back in the fifties, this boy really
has taken to Marathon running like a duck to orange! He's one of those
rare natural athletes whose taken a long time to find his ideal distance. But
now in his mid-thirties he is maturing like a fine wine and just gets better
with every performance. Look at that power! I think Molesworth could well
be on the way to a personal best here! He's destroyed the rest of the feild!
Look at those legs! Already he's covered over twenty miles on a World
Record Shedule and he's still full of running . . . .

At this point, fifty yards down Arbutus Ave I had to lean
against a tree to get my breath back.

Then when I started again I jarred something in my spine.

I attracted the attension of the owner of the front garden into
which I managed to crawl. He phoned for Louise, who came
and picked me up in the car.

I told her I'd felt a severe pain in the chestal area, and she
hasnt mentioned jogging again since. (Mind you, she does leave
lots of insurance brochures lying about.)

CRICKET is a game of unbelievable tedeum and one of the
great bennefits of getting older is that you no longer have to
play it.

The fact that our national game lasts five days is a sad comment on the dillatery nature of our national character (and
probably the explaination of much of our currant economic
mallaise).

But because cricket involves so much standing around doing
nothing and recquires absolutely no fitness at all, various of my
contemperaries are quite attracted to it. They are seduced by
television commercials for beer, cheese, pickles, ect. into im-
agining a game of cricket will be a summer iddyl on the village
green.

Even a slob like Timothy Peason, outwardly a level-headed
sort of bloke, gets keen on this fatuos passtime. Obviously the
main appeal for him is the beer afterwards, but he does seem
to take the game quite seriously too.

Sharon produces imaculate white kit for him every weekend
and he makes it a point of honour to cover it imediately with
as many grass-stains as possible. He also (because he is a bowler)
rubs a brickred streak down his crutch (for reasons aparent only

to another bowler). He holds his trousers up round his massive paunch with his OCT (Old Custardian Tie) and wears a floppy white hat, which makes him look like a melting icecream.

When he bowls he thunders up to the crease like a hipoppotamos at full throttle. It cannot be healthy for a man of his age.

Like most cricketters he is obsessed with numbers and spends all his time working out his batting averige, his bowling averige, his catching averige, his feilding averige, his dropped-catching averige, his misfeilding averige, his number-of-times-for-hitching-up-his-OCT-round-his-paunch averige, ect., ect., ect. (Sharon should never have given him that caculater for his birthday.)

From what I have seen of him playing, 0 has changed since St Cs days. The three basic rules of schoolboy cricket are still obeyed.

1 When bowling: Heavy breathing, grunting and shouting OWZATTT!!! at every conceivable oportunity are much more important than accuracy.
2 When batting: Each misshit (if your still in) should be followed by a practise stroke, to indicate that you know what you should have done and are merely peplexed that it didn't work.
3 When feilding: It is more important to throw yourself dramaticly after the ball than actually to stop it.

Timothy Peason still follows all these precepts implicitly.

Why does he do it? Why does he still play? Surely he didn't believe all that guff we were fed at St Cs about cricket reflecting LIFE (though come to think of it LIFE is pretty boring and pointless, so maybe there was something in it after all).

I have taxed him on this matter (i.e. why he continues to play now its no longer compulsery), but he always prooves evasive. I fear his reasons are wholey sentimental – i.e. he really goes for all that hourtoplayandthelastmansin, thwonk of willowon-leather, church clock and istherehoneystillfortea rubbish – and is afraid I would laugh if he told me the truth.*

BADMINTON is a game of unbelievable wetness, so guess

* He is right – Ed.

who plays it? Yes, you have it in one – Basil Fotherington-Thomas, the man who makes Cliff Richard look abraisive and gritty.

He and Araminta (and undoutedly Arrabella) are members of a club in Wimbledon and play avidly. It suits them. Maybe it is the similarity of badminton raquette and shuttlecock to butterfly net and butterfly that makes it seem so apt, but certainly bearing his hairless knees and prancing round after a feathery thing fits the image of the Basil I have always known.

They play at least twice a week and when they have worked themselves up into a larther of mutual congratulation (I cannot imagine them actually sweating – it is not a Fotherington-Thomas thing to do), they go to the club bar and drink LIMEJUICE AND SODA!

This seems to me a complete abneggation (classy word, huh?) of the purpose of taking exercice. Its bad enough doing it anyway but if you dont have a few beers afterwards what is the point, I ask you?

But that's what they do. A pint of limejuice and soda each, then back home for a healthgiving slice of soyerbean and sea-weed quishe.

I know this routine, because though it hurts me to confess, I have actually DONE IT.

For a long time Basil had been trying to lure me out onto the badminton court. He seems to take my subsidense into paunchy torpour personally and feel he has to DO SOMETHING ABOUT IT.

One ungarded moment he caught me on the phone at GBH.

'Hello,' I said, expecting a call from the Cheif Clerk, Invoice Docketting (Internal). 'Nigel Molesworth.'

'Hello, Nigel,' Basil bubbled. 'How *super* to hear your voice.' (Once again he meant it. Ugh.)

I grunted noncommittley.

'Nigel, how about a game of badminton?'

'Erg?'

'It's a *super* game. I'm sure you'd enjoy it. Keeps you fit, too. You know, *mens sauna in corpore sauna* and have you made a will yet?'

When in the changing room I see how puny Basil's body still is, so I dont feel as bad about agreing to play. I try not to ripple my mussels overostentaciously – do not want to depress him too much. I take a few experimental swishes with the borrowed raquette and think maybe this will be all right after all.

We get onto the court and he explains the rules. This takes some time. I am vaguely aware of the rules of tennis, but that apears not to help. Badminton is diffrent for no reason that I can see except PEVERSENESS.

Then we start to play, the craggy splendor of my body pitted against the diaphonous whispiness of his.

IT IS AMAZING. He beats me easily. Not only beats me, trounces me. Tries giving me ten points start and still beats me.

WHAT HAS HAPPENED TO HIM? Where is the weed who wandered round the football feild effeetly saying, 'Hello clouds hello sky'? He is transformed into a finely-tuned sports-machine who manages to be all over the court at the same time, and who has the gaul to say 'WelldoneNigelgood-shot!' everytime I even hit the shuttlecock. It is DEMEENING.

Afterwards he throws his arm round my shoulders in a gesture of unwelcome *cammerarderie* and says, 'We must do it again, Nigel. You were getting *hetter* in that last game!' (i.e. I scored 1 pt).

I try not to weeze too obviously and limp beside him (really hurts the back of the calves, badminton).

In the bar before I can say what I want I find he has bought me a pt of limejuice and soda. Araminta and Arrabella join us and for half an hour they all agree how wonderful life is.

Then just when I think I can politely stagger home, the awfulness of the evening is compounded by an invitation to go back and share their quishe and try their first bottle of Banana and Eldaflower Wine (which should be 'jolly nearly ready' says Basil).

In my reduced state I am unable to think of an excuse quick enough.

UGHHHHH!!!

SQUASH is Darryl Pacey's game because he read in *The Complete Young Executive's Manuel* (pub. Grabber & Grabber @ £8.95) the following passage: '*It is important for a young executive to keep fit, and playing competative games is good training for the competative stresses of his working life. But the young executive must always be consious of the cost of his time, so concentrate on games which acheeve the maximum of exercice in the minimum time. Of these squash is one of the most efficcient.'*

So twice a week Darryl uses his lunchhour in a diffrent way from his usual habit (i.e. he doesnt work through it) and goes down to the basement of GBH House to the squash court.

This is how he fits it into his shedule:

1.00 p.m. Leave Invoice Docketting (Internal) Dept. on the 11th floor.
1.03 p.m. Arrive squash court changing room in basement. Change.
1.05 p.m. Enter squash court. Play vigourously.
1.45 p.m. Stop playing. Commiserate with opponent.
1.46 p.m. Shower.
1.47 p.m. Change back into thrusting young executive kit.
1.49 p.m. Catch lift back up to 11th floor.
1.52 p.m. Back behind desk in Invoice Docketting (Internal) Dept.
1.59 p.m. Look up from work and smile rightiously as other gnomes begin to return from lunch.
2.48 p.m. Look up from work and smile ingraciatingly as Grint returns from lunch.
3.11 p.m. Look up from work and smile pittyingly as N. Molesworth returns from lunch.

He did actually once lure me down onto the squash court for a game, but that is all I am prepared to tell you. I dont want intrusions into my private grief. (Any way he is a LOT YOUNGER than me.)

FOOTBALL, i.e. soccer, is very boring and I dont know how people manage to get so exited about 'Match of the Day' (though I suppose it is a good oportunity to have a few beers and ignor ones wife).

St Cs really strangled at birth any potencial love of the game, though my interest did flicker briefly when Tristram was small and I found I could dodge round him like Pelle and always get the ball from him by a sything tackle. As hes got bigger he has developped the ability to do that to me and my interest in the game has once again wained. (Though like everyone else I can still build up a good zenophobiac head of steam when the World Cup comes round.)

RUGBY is a tough game for masoschists. It is best played by other people. Fortunatley I am now too old for anyone to expect me to play it, so I can enjoy the only good bits – which are standing on the touchline (or sitting in front of the telly) with a pt of beer shouting COMEONWHEREAREYOU-TACKLEHIMTACKLEHIMYOUGREATOAF for all the world like a St Cs sports master.

Ruby has social caché. It is played by soliciters and account-ants and doctors who SPEAK FRIGHTFULLY WELL* when inteviewed by some television lacky. People like Darryl Pacey did not play rugby at their so-called schools so I ocasion-ally gain a cheap moment of superiority by commenting on the weekend international just to see the atavistic awe of centuries of subserviance in his proletarean face. (Not of course that I'm a snob, Louise looks after the snobbery in our family.)

GOLF is the only sport which you can play whilst smoking. It is not a game: like the Masons, Rotary Clubs ect., it is a mutual backscratching institution for businessmen. The scorecards tend to read:

17th Hole (OWL'S SPORRAN)   7 strokes and £7 trillion
                                                 contract signed.

The skill in businessgolf is knowing who to beat and who not to beat. Darryl Pacey, needless to say, is learning to play because he read in *The Executive's Guide to Toadying* (pub. Grabber & Grabber @ £17.95) that it is a useful executive accomplishe-ment. He was once invited out for a round with Grint and managed to lose every hole with apalling sycaphancy. (The week before he'd invited me out for a round – as a rehearsal for his encounter with Grint – and I managed to lose every hole with no sycaphancy at all. No justice is there?)

* Exept for the Welch ones, but all the Welch speak pretty peculierly, any way. – Ed.

TENNIS is a game for teenagers trying to pick up members of the opposite sex down at the Tennis Club. At least thats how I remember it. Louise and I recently joined the local Tennis Club, but *with her there* I couldnt really apreciate all the golden-thighed teenage girls, so it all seemed a bit pointless.

FEILD SPORTS are what Grabber does all the time. They are things like SHOOTING partridges and peacocks and peasants on his country estate, FISHING for trout with flies called March Hare, Stuffed Olive, Dry Sherry, Red Setter and Brown Winsor, HUNTING foxes for no very clear reason, ect., ect., ect.

Since they all involve having trillions of pounds, they do not impinge on my life much and I am not very inclined to think of them as SPORTS at all (FUMES OF JEALOUSY).

OF COURSE NOWADAYS ONE HAS TO FACE IT – SPORT IS NO LONGER A PARTICIPENT ACTIVITY. It is just something to watch on the television.

It is in fact the modern equivalent of *pane et circumstances*. (You see, just when you'd written me off as uncultured, I come up with a classical illusion like that to really shake you.) Oh yes, sportsmen on the television screen are the GLADIATORS OF TODAY and their sucess depends, like that of the gladiators of old, on the whims, the thumbs-up or thumbs-down, of the public. (This bit is good.) It is no longer the world of *Tom Browns Schooldays* (pub. Grabber & Grabber Classic Reprints @ £8.95); Flashmans values have taken over. No athlete these days is content with hiscaptainshandonhisshouldersmote; even the tasseledcap and the ficklewhatnotofaseasonsthingie are inadaquate; what they demand now is a three trillion pounds *per anum* contract for liver salts.

The really big growth industry in sport is for fashion designers inventing new places to put brand names on sports garments. Soon they will actualy tatoo them onto the sportsmen themselves, so that a change of sponsership will involve plastic surgery.

I DO NOT MIND ALL THIS.

I can at least understand it. When people are running or whatever for SHEER NAKED GREED it makes much more sense than when they're running or whatever for vaigue reasons of sportsmanship, 'proving something to myself' or, as some of them have the nerve to maintain – FUN!

At least nowadays you know where you are. There is less and less disguise of the comercial aspect of sport. You have only to switch on your television on a Saturday afternoon to hear this sort of thing . . .

PRESENTER (WEARING A SUIT WHOSE PATTERN IS MADE UP OF THE WORDS 'GRABBER SPORTS-WARE FOR REAL SPORTSMEN'): *Good afternoon, and what an afternoon of sport we have for you this afternoon! First we go to the Royal and Ancient at St Andrews for the Jacobs Chocolate Golf. Then we'll be at Cowdrey Park for some first-class Polo (The Mint With the Hole), onto Penzants for the Lever Brothers Surf-Riding Competition, to Worthing for the All-England Tuppaware Bowls Championship, and then of course the highlights of the Sun-fresh Lemon Squash Tournement . . . .*

The other good thing they always have on these programmes is an inteview with some Old Fogey Who Used To Be Good At Something In The Past about the increasing comercialism of sport. These are always great fun, because whatever the OF-WUTBGAS says, you can imagine exactly what he is really thinking and see him EATING HIS HEART OUT . . . .

INTEVIEWER

Well, Bill, of course the game has changed a lot since you were in the national team. Now these youngesters can make so much money out of it, do you think it's had an affect on the sport?

OFWUTBGAS	*Real thoughts*
Well, Brian, I think what has gone out of the game is the sense of fun. I mean when I played, I did it for enjoyment. O.K., I was honoured to represent my country, but it was just another game and you know the aim was simply to do	Of course it has, you fool. The thought of all these horrible little erks making all that money and swanking around in Mercedes and going out with film stars and going to posh nightclubs and having investment advisers to tell them what to do with all

ones best and have a good work-out with the other chaps. Of course, the competative element was there, it really mattered, but we never forgot it was a game and our primery aim was to get on with it, give of our best, and then go out for a few beers, get to know the other fellows . . . I think what's gone out of the game, in a word, is *camerarderie*. Of course, I don't regret it. I had a good innings . . . ect., ect., ect. . . . .

their loot makes me want to bloody puke. When I think of all that they're getting – massive salaries, apearence money, huge endorcement contracts, while I'm reduced to scraping and saving and sitting in television studios at inconveniant times, giving stupid inteviews like this for a few bob. I'm not even famous enough to get booked for one of those Celebritty Golf Tournements. The fees for for those are really worth having . . . ect., ect., ect . . . [FUMES OF JEALOUSY]

I enjoy watching Saturday afternoon sport for things like that. In fact, I enjoy it for most things – not because I'm interested in the actual games, but its nice and mindless and undermanding and it changes quite often. Pleasant shifting pattens of colour, a glass in one hand, Tristram and Lucinda bought off with a quid to go down to the sweetshop, Louise out at a matinee at the Academy Two – that must be one of my visions of perfection.

And if to that is added not only real sport but RUBBISH-SPORT, then it's even better.

RUBBISHSPORT is a growing trend in television for con-tests in which people who are GOOD AT SOMETHING have to do things that they're NO GOOD AT ALL AT. So racing-drivers have to polevalt, swimmers play tennis, jockys play pro-celebrity snap ect. Its also extended to people who have nothing to do with sport at all, but are just famous for being on television. So someone who was *awfully good as Macbeth* will have to run the 100 meters High Hurdles, or a disc jocky will have to play water-polo, or a newsreader throw the javellin.

This is all in keeping with the BASIC AIM OF TELE-VISION, which is: TO MAKE PEOPLE LOOK SILLY.

And it's great fun.

So a bit of RUBBISHSPORT should certainly be added to create my ideal Saturday afternoon.

But I very rarely get it.

Tristram and Lucinda will start fighting or need attension for some other reason. Or if they keep quiet, Louise will come home early and catch me at it.

'Oh really, Nigel, how you can just sit and watch television when there's so much to do! I thought you were going to start stripping the cuboard in Lucindas room, and then get on with painting the telephone-alcove with that Simmered Rattattoui paint we bought at Grabbers. . . . Or if you insist on watching television why do you rot your mind with things like this? There's a repeat on BBC2 at *this very moment* of a fascinating Access programme in which twelve unemployed youths from Toxteth are positting the view that greater devolution of government could only bennefit local comunities by bringing burocracy into more accesible areas of grassroots reaction-pattens. I mean if you were taking time off to watch that I would understand. But this sort of MINDLESS RUBBISH. . . .' ect., ect., ect.

Oh dear. It's always like that.

For a moment I even contemplate PLAYING sport. Even cricket. I begin to see its appeal. It does get you out of the house for longer than almost any other game. (But, knowing my luck, if I did start playing, Louise would insist on coming along too to bully the teas.)

9

LEISURE

*Or, Nigel's Very Into Beermats,
Actualy*

LEISURE is what you fill in the gaps between doing things
you have to do with. Increasing leisure is supposed to be a
phenomenon of modern life. Some people aparently find it a
problem knowing what to do with it all.

I am not one of their number. I enjoy leisure so long as it
doesnt involve doing anything (in fact ideally not doing anything
in front of the television with a pt in my hand).

But there are people who work much harder at their leisure
than they do at their work. (Actualy, even watching television
can be pretty hard work sometimes – viz. when certain Arts
Programmes are on or some of those intense foreign movies
with subtitles which Louise claims to enjoy so much and makes
me watch 'in the forlorn hope that it might IMPROVE YOUR
MIND a little, Nigel.')

Of all leisure activities in this country, WATCHING TELE-
VISION is the commonest.

Louise thinks most of it is VERY COMMON INDEED
(and that's about as low as you can go on Louise's scale of
values). She and I, as you will have gathered, have divergant
views on what television is for.

I see it as a RELAXANT, a kind of visual Vallium which
sends waves of mediocrity washing over the body, reducing it
to a state of torper.

Louise, on the other hand, regards it as a MEDIUM OF
EDUCATION and has great contemt for any programme that
has not got a HIGH INFORMATIONAL CONTENT (i.e.
anything I might want to watch).

The difference in our attitudes can best be demonstrated by

The difference in our attitudes can best be demonstrated by listing the sort of programmes we each like to watch . . . .

My Ideal Evening's Television	Louise's Ideal Evening's Television
7.00 ATHELETICS: Lots of very fit people running very hard while I slump in an armchair with a drink.	**7.00 WHITHER?:** Does the changing roll of religion in society mean that we should rethink our attitudes to monnotheism? Or not?
7.30 TOP OF THE POPS: A show to give me the allusion that I am still part of the SCENE (and full of women in tight blowzes).	**7.30 ISSUE:** A documentry exposing the lack of government controls over harmful additives in cieling tile adehsive and likely ghastly consequences.
8.00 OH NO, IT'S A SIT-COM!: Something undermanding about a roll-reversal couple who have remarried each other and are trying to give up smoking.	**8.00 ABSTRUSE:** The Arts Magazine, feauturing LADISLAV VRONSPOTSCH, Polish exponent of Imobile Mime, part of MAATTII HAAVABITTAA'S Masterclass for counter-tenners, the KLUNTSCH RETRASPECTIVE at the I.C.A. and the new All-Vynil production of THE RING CYCLE from Beirut.
8.30 PEOPLE ARE FUNNY: A game show in which contestants with an I.Q. of 0.0000000000001 are rituraly humilliated.	
9.00 POLICE SERIES: Bland, glossy American import about a busty crimebuster bringing to justice the men who keep stealing her blowze.	**9.00 THE NEWS:** The latest headlines, with seering and depressing up-to-the-minute comments on the state of the world.

10.00 SNOOKER : Soft
voices and nice moving
colours, the ideal
accompanyment to a
quiet drink.

10.30 WRESTLING :
From the Baths Hall,
Bootle, feauturing a
Heavyweight Contest
between
PSYCOPATH
SIMKINS and
COMBINE
HARVESTER
HIGGS.

11.00 FILM : 'A
FISTFUL OF
DALLAS' (1969) :
Spagetti Western full
of gratiutous violence,
floggings, hangings,
women having their
blowzes ripped off,
ect.
THE MAN ...CHUCK STAKE
THE WOMAN ....
.............DORITA Y PEPE
THE FAT MAYOR ....
..........LASAGNA VERDDE
THE THIN LUNATIC ......
.... OSSO BUCO
34th showing on
British Television

12.30 CARTOON : TOM
& GERRY

12.35 CLOSEDOWN

9.25 FILM : 'NGUSHU
MONABANGI' (1973)
KANGO
SUKIYAKI'S sensative
story of a one-legged
novice monk and the
young girl he meets who
thinks she is a mangolia
tree. Starring
NITZAGOSHI
KOKU and
GUGNOKI
MUSHATUNGORA.
(With subtitles.) First
showing on British
Television.

11.30 CONCERN : A
programme about other
people's sufferrings to
give you the allusion
that you have a social
consience. Programme
17 : THE PROBLEMS
PENSIONERS HAVE
WITH
SUPERMARKET
TROLLIES.

12.05 OPEN UNIVERSITY:
WITTGENSTIEN –
Some Annomalies and
Reappraisles.

12.30 POEM : 'Diaganal
Yesterdays', translated
from the Icelandic.

12.35 CLOSEDOWN

(The trouble is we've only got one television, so the diffrence in our tastes is another potencial source of martial conflict.)

In theory these days its possible to shedule your own IDEAL EVENING'S TELEVISION by using a videorecorder, but I cant ever see myself getting sufficiently organised to record the right programmes at the right time. (Anyway, we havent got one.)

But I have noticed that people who do own videorecorders very quickly become profficient in letting everyone KNOW the fact. 30 secs is the max. a conversation is allowed to go without referrence being made to the machine.

ALLOW ME TO DEMONSTRATE.

1 When the conversation is actually about television, the VIDEORECORDER-DROP is easy.

e.g. FEED   Did you see that programme last night about reesus monkeys?

    RESPONCE   No. I'm going to see it tonight.

or: FEED   I hope you didnt mind comeing out to dinner tonight and missing the Snooker.

    RESPONCE   I'm not missing it.

2 When television is not directly mentioned the VIDEORECORDER-DROP is more difficult, but this does not deter the skilled practitioner.

e.g. FEED   Do you suffer from insomnia?

    RESPONCE   Ocassionaly. But when I do I just go downstairs and catch up on all the television programmes I've missed.

or: FEED   I think you've got impetigoe.

    RESPONCE   Oh dear. I was watching a programme about that only yesterday before breakfast.

3 The most shameless videorecorder-owners dont bother to wait for even the most obscure feeds. Their VIDEO-RECORDER-DROP is a favorite *non sequitter* with which they interrupt every conversation at will.

e.g. Oh dam! There's something on the telly at the moment I meant to be recording.

or (most blatant of all): I've got a videorecorder!!!

I personally feel that this sort of CONSPICUOUS CON-SUMERISM is quite disgusting. Needless to say, my apalling brother Steve has lots of videorecorders (and lots of porno-graphic casettes too, come to that – FUMES OF JEALOUSY).

Another popular leisure activity is COLLECTING THINGS.

This is a dubius practise about which psycologists e.g. Sig-ismund Freud, Larry Adler ect. have a lot to say. The need to horde possessions in this way is clearly compensation for a personality deficiency. (cf. S. FREUD – *The Case of the Com-pulsive Numismattist* pub. Grabber & Grabber @ £75).

I do not collect anything (well, exept beermats, but that is only a ruse to explain to Louise the mesmerric affect pubs have over me – actualy I'm rather afraid its a ruse shes beginning to see through but I dont want to worry you with my problems). This is clearly a sign that I have a well-intergrated personality (a fact obvious I would have thought to the meanest interlect).

But I do know people who suffer from *accumulomania* (being the Latin term for this disorder).

That little grammer school erk DARRYL PACEY collects books on Management Tecniques ect., but that doesnt really count because the true *collectofile* doesnt collect anything USE-FUL and Darryl thinks his books will be instrumental in giving him a leg-up the Management Ladder at GBH. (He is of course wrong.)

GRABBER AND FELICITIAH collect little nick-nacks like diamond tiaras, Krugeränds, Japanese *nestuke*, Fabargee eggs ect., but these dont count either because they are IN-VESTMENTS, insuring that their income goes up a trillion pounds *per anum*. Anyway, they dont do any of the searching out and buying themselves; that is all dealt with by the Little Man In Charge of Collecting.

MY APALLING BROTHER STEVE collects trillions of LPs of frightful Heavy Metal Music, which I would have thought is about as useless as you can get, but he claims he NEEDS THEM FOR HIS WORK. Since the precise nature of his work is vailed in secrecy and (probably) criminality, this is hard to proove. But he is something to do with immoral exploitation of pop groups, so I have to give him the bennefit of the doubt about the LPs.

(Insidentaly, I think I should make clear at this point that I DO NOT APPROVE OF MY BROTHER'S LIFESTYLE.

All that easy money and all those easy women cannot be good for the developement of a character whose foundations were so firmly laid all those years ago at St Cs. I keep telling him that he is RIDING FOR A FALL, though to date there's no sign of it coming – FUMES OF JEALOUSY.)

But if you want to find real examples of *accumulomania* you have to look at – predictabley enough – the Fotherington-Thomases and – of all people – TIMOTHY PEASON!!!

Now this amazes me. I mean Peason's a reasonabley level-headed sort of bloke. He's not very bright of course . . . and O.K., he's an accountant, but he's learnt to live with these disabilities and to lead an almost normal life. And yet he has these bazaar WARPS OF PERSONALITY, like volunterily playing cricket and – it hurts me to admit this of a friend – COLLECTING FIFTIES EPHEMERA!

The psychological basis for this is quite simple as I keep telling him – he does it because he *is* a piece of Fifties Ephemera.

But my words do not deter him – he still chases round junk markets searching out old posters, magazines, 78s ect. And as if that wasnt bad enough, he goes to CONVENTIONS OF LIKEMINDED LOONIES middleaged men with the sad remnants of their hair quiffed up, dressed in long jackets, bootlace ties, flourescent socks ect.

'YOU ARE MAKING A FOOL OF YOURSELF,' I rail at him. 'YOU ARE TRYING TO RECAPTURE A PART OF YOUR YOUTH THAT NEVER EXISTED. BE-CAUSE YOU WENT TO PONSY PRIVATE SCHOOLS YOU NEVER MIXED WITH THE SORT OF RIFFRAFF YOU ARE NOW TRYING TO EMMULATE. IT IS TOO LATE FOR YOU TO BECOME ELVIS PRESLEY.'

Bur he does not listen. It is disasterous. (Actualy the only good thing about it is he takes Sharon with him and stilleto heels, waspie belts and tight sweaters LOOK REALLY GOOD on her.)

It is sad to see an otherwise normal bloke in the throws of such a passion. HE NEEDS HELP. I have done my best to reason with him . . . .

(The scene is the consultingroom of Doktor Ernst Molesvorthovich. The eminant doktor sits in a high-backed chair, his pencil poised allertly over his notebook. His patient, Peason, is slumped on the leather couch, giving his usual impression of a dead duvet.)

DOKTOR   Und ven dis zis obsesion viz sings of ze Fifties start?

PEASON   Er . . . well . . . in the Fifties, I suppose.

DOKTOR   *(quick as a flash)* Not before?

PEASON   Well . . . er . . . no. I mean, I was only five when the Fifties started.

DOKTOR   AHAH! *(he makes a note of this very signifficant fact that he has illicitted.)* Und during your first fife years, Herr Peason, did you ever feel any nostaglia for ze *eighteen*-fifties?

PEASON   Well, no. I mean, I wasnt borne, was I?

DOKTOR   *(laughing indulgently at this simplistic response)* Ha, ha, Herr Peason. People are zo shortsighted. Your life does not begin at birz. Ze prenatel influences are much more important. Ven you emerge from ze woomb, ze main outlines of your character haf already been long established. Vich is vy I ask about ze *eighteen*-fifties . . . .

PEASON   But my mother wasnt even alive in the eighteen-fifties.

DOKTOR   It is not your muzzer I am interested in. Perhaps your *grand*muzzer. Perhaps your *great*grandmuzzer. Who knows vot happens in ze dark resesses of ze pysche, ha, ha. Ve must delve back a long way, Herr Peason, to find ze sauce of ze problem.

PEASON   But that'll take forever.

DOKTOR   I haf all ze time in ze world, Herr Peason.* Now vere shall ve start?

* Zo he should haf at ze rate he iz paid per hour. – Ed.

PEASON	How about the Coach and Hounds? I'm dying for a pt.
DOKTOR	Ah. O vell. O.K. *(exeunt to the Coach and Hounds for the rest of the evening.)*

That's the trouble – whenever I try to talk seriously to Peason about his ghastly condition, he waylays me and the subject gets changed . . . .

BASIL AND ARAMINTA FOTHERINGTON-THO-MAS'S collecting bug expresses itself differently. They are always ON THE LOOKOUT for OBJECTS to make their house look even more like a cowshed.

This means they spend a lot of time rooting round junkshops. It must be wonderful! for the dealers who see them coming. (*'Ho, ho, this looks a likely couple. Good, I can unload all my rubbish on them. Great, soon I will be able to buy another chateaux in the Dordonge. Yes, sir, madame, and what were you looking for?'*)

The result is that Basil and Araminta always return home with arms full of wormey carpenters planes, chipped enammel signs, rusty wheelright's spoke-crimpers, cracked larboard cottle-wafflers, perished coffinmakers' corbulating-bands ect.

'Oh, what a lovely PIECE! Weren't we lucky!' coos Araminta.

'Oh, wonderful!' cries Basil. 'Life is wonderful!'

'Marvellous!' gushes Arrabella, whose almost definately there too.

'Thoby! Ghislane! Come and see what Mama and Papa have bought!'

'Now where shall we put it? How about over on that mud-coloured wall between the Northumberian boilermakers trumbling-spanner and the Cornish weaver's reverse-lipping-plunger?'

'Oh, Araminta, what a wonderful eye you have for compo-sition? I will sand it down seven trillion times, give it four trillion coats of bees wax and fix it up there immediately! Oh, how lucky I am to have such a wife! (ARAMINTA SIMPERS) And such a sister! (ARRABELLA SIMPERS) And such children! (THOBY AND GHISLANE SIMPER*) Oh how lucky I am!'

ERGH . . . .

I was going to tell you more about the Fotherington-Thomases leisure activities (country-dancing, manufacture of corn-dollies, traceing lay-lines, asterology ect.) but I'm afraid my nerve is not strong enough.

DARRYLANDCARRYL dont have any leisure in the real sense, but they do devote some of their evenings to playing BRIDGE, a cardgame of quite incredible tedeum. Darryl only does it because he thinks it will be a useful executive accomplishement and help him GET ON. He has taught himself from *Grabber's Guide To Bridge* (The AWOL System) (published by Messrs Grabber & Grabber @ £10.95).

Louise would like to play. She thinks its the kind of thing that will comfort her in her old age. Also her unnerrring nose for such things tells her it has SNOB APPEAL.

We once went along to Darrylandcarryls for an evening's bridge, but it was not a success. I have to confess that that was my fault. I had great difficulty in understanding the rules and when I did understand I couldnt see the point of them. So I came up with a much simpler way of playing the game, but I couldnt persuade the others to try it. Louise got pretty cross.

Card-games I'm afraid are not for me. Board-games though are a different matter . . . .

---

* This involves no change for them. It is their normal expression. – Ed.

THE MOLESWORTH IDEAL BOARD-GAME:

Pints & Chasers

(A Game for 1 or more Players)

RULES:

The aim of the game is not to get HOME, because

a) That means you will have to stop drinking, and

b) Louise will be there.

The game is played like Snakes & Ladders, counters* being moved a number of squares acording to the throw of a dice†. Landing on a PINT square means that the player has to down a pint of beer; landing on a CHASER square means a whisky.

The game is said to be finished when one of the players is unable to continue. The player is said to be finished then too.

PATS. PENDING.

* You do not have to use counters – Ed.
† Or dice. Timothy Peason and I usually dispense with both – Ed.

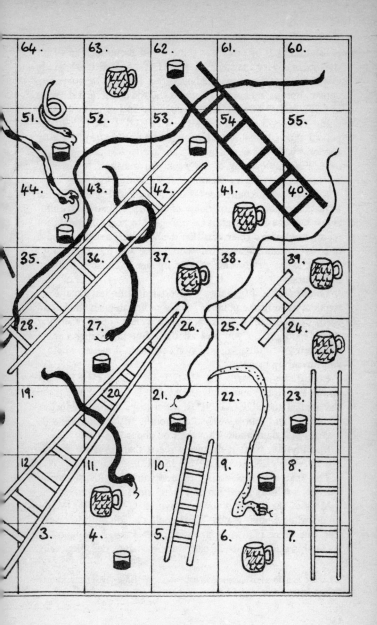

LOUISE actualy has a leisure activity of her own. (At one point, enthused by talking to some friend about Women's Lib, she became very insistent on HAVING A LIFE OF HER OWN. 'It's very important, Nigel, that I should be a separate entitty, not just an apendage of you and the children. I do want to GET MY OWN THINGS GOING. So I'm going to start doing THINGS ON MY OWN, WITHOUT YOU.' At this point I showed what a modern undestanding husband I am by agreeing with her completely. 'Yes, great, do things on your own. Yes, any evening of the week you want to.' It was only when I suggested *every* evening that she got narked.)

Anyway, what Louise does is sing in a choir. I cannot see the attraction of this. My experiense of singing, still strongly influenced by Miss Pringle at St Cs who used to beat out the rythm on my head with a ruler, was that the best thing to do was stand next to someone who actualy could sing and mouthe lustily. And it seems pretty daft to give up one evening a week to moutheing.

Louise sees it differently. I have tried to undestand the attraction, even to the point of talking to her about it, but to no avail. I suppose if I could sing, I could see the appeal of singing solos, spotlight on you and all that. But just being one of hundreds . . . I dont know, I cant see that it'd matter whether you turned up or not.

Louise says its partly the MAGIC OF THE MUSIC (lost on me I'm afraid) and partly the SOCIAL SIDE. Since those I've met of the SOCIAL SIDE seem to be anguler spinsters (if female) and immaciated spotty youths with string vests (if male), I still dont know what she's on about.

But anyway, what it means to me is that EVERY WEDNESDAY EVENING LOUISE IS OUT.

This inables me to indulge in *my* leisure activities – having a drink, watching television and fantesising.

Most of the fantesies involve inviting OTHER WOMEN round while Louise is out. What couldn't I do with Charleen from the office for two hours at home?* I also have fantesies about this sixteen-year-old babysitter we have. Cor, she really

* That is a retorical question. I dont want my fantesy shattered by any realistic answers thankyou – Ed.

is something. Not every man of my age gets creatures like that walking into his sittingroom.

The trouble is of course that normally when she arrives I am just about to go out with Louise, which is an imediate deterent to lustful imaginings. And since she only lives up the road, I dont even get a chance to drive her home.

But Wednesday nights I fantesise about asking her in. I'm sure at sixteen she is longing for a sauve sophisticated man-of-the-world to innitiate her in the WAYS OF LOVE. Who better than me with my worldweary *savoie-fair*, vast experience, exceptional looks, ect.?

The trouble is, how do I get her to come round? Getting someone in to babysit while I'm actualy there might make a woman with a less suspicious nature than Louise's smell a rat. And with Louise herself . . . .

So the relationship remains at fantesy level, which is probably just as well.

I do enjoy my Wednesday evenings, though.

AMATEUR DRAMATICS. Now it's confession time. Get ready for the revelation. O.K.?

Once I – even I, Nigel Molesworth – TOOK PART IN AMATEUR DRAMATICS!

It was not a voluntery action. (Indeed I wonder whether I've made any voluntery actions since Louise decided we should get married.) It arose out of one of Louise's dinner parties. As usual she had surounded our table with all available affected twits and psueds – incl. the director of the latest production for The Wimbledon Thespians. He was called Byron. (Well, he wasnt realy – he was realy called Brian – but one of the first rules of Amatuer Dramatics is that you change your name to something MORE ARTISTIC. The second rule is that you wear scarfs round your neck and sandals, but one thing at a time.) He was complaining that he was having difficulty in finding suficcient men for the *challenging* new play he was putting on, *Womb Service* by local author Dorcas De Nice (Real Name: Dorothy Dennis). The trouble was that the play, modelled on Greek theatre, recquired a Chorus of Sperms and he felt that to cast these out of the enormous surplice of single ladies which all Amatuer Dramatic Societies have WOULD BE GOING AGAINST THE AUTHORS' INTENTIONS.

Where, oh where was he going to find three more Sperms in Wimbledon?

I bit back the ready reposte which sprang to my lips and was amazed to hear Louise saying, 'Oh, I'm sure Nigel would help you out. He never does anything USEFUL in the evenings. I'm sure being in the CHALLENGING PLAY you describe would do him a lot of good. You'll help Byron out, WON'T YOU, NIGEL?'

(Once again I wished that I'd known Louise when I was doing Latin. That was a perfect example of a QUESTION EXPECTING THE ANSWER YES.)

But I wasnt going to be caught that way. I opened my mouth to say exactly what I thought of Louise's proposal, but before it could shape words, Byron's came gushing forth.

'Oh, Niggles! You absolute darling! Now I've only got two more Sperms to find!'

Well . . . .

Louise insisted that I do it. ('You did give your word, Nigel.' 'Not true,' I cried valiently, 'not true!' But to no avail.) So I had to turn up to these rehearsals in some church hall full of Mos and Vees and Ivans and Dorindas and Shads and Flicks and Chips and Salvadors and Nitas and Frayas and Alexes and Juliuses, all dressed in scarfs round their necks and sandals. I knew from the start that it was not my scene, but LOUISE HAD SPOKEN.

Ugh, the stuff I had to learn! Dorcas De Nice's so-called play was in so-called verse and the terrible thing is I still remember it. Much more important things – like the words of dirty limericks Timothy Peason tells me – my tired old brain cannot retain, but Dorcas De Nice's lines are fixed on the surface of my mind like the scars of a flogging.*

I can remember our first entrance with ghastly clarity . . . .

* That's not bad. I quite like that – Ed.

(Scene: The womb. Enter a chorus of sperms.)

SPERMS *(tutti)* Oh, we are the men of tomorrow,
                Bearers of joy or of sorrow.
                We're the bare essentials
                Of unrealised potential.
                Some of us will die and some
                Will be the shape of things to come.
                You cant deny the human race, it
                Will be run. Oh, can you face it?
                Our future's dire. Our fate apalls.
                We see it in our cristal balls . . . .

(I got into bad odor at my first rehearsal at this point, because I thought the above line was – and not before time – A JOKE. So I played it for a laugh and brought down on my head the wroth of Byron and Dorcas and Mo and Vee and Ivan and Dorinda and Shad and Flick and Chip and Salvador and Nita and Fraya and Alex and Julius and the rest of them. Therafter at rehearsals I kept quiet.)

The whole thing got worse as we drew nearer to our opening (as they all called it). I still remember with a shudder when they first showed us our costumes.

I HAD TO WEAR TIGHTS!

Ugh. I still wake up in the night sweating at the thought.

But the worst thing about it was trying to keep the fact that I was in it from various people I knew, esp. T. Peason. I could never have held my head up again if he'd found out what I was up to.

I managed to keep him in the dark by the clever ruse of voluntiering to help with the publicity. This meant I found out where the Publicity Manager (Mo or Ivan or Shad or Chip or Salvador or Alex or Julius – I forget which) was going to stick up the posters for the show and followed round half an hour after him RIPPING THEM ALL DOWN.

The performances were even more excrusiating than the rehearsals. I blackened my face and hid behind the other Sperms all the time, but I still had this terrible nightmare of looking down into the auditoreum one night and seeing Peason's face (which even now bears a striking ressemblance to a squished tomatoe) staring up at me.

But the worst moment of all came at the Cast Party. I suppose, given a few drinks and all the unattached Vees and Dorindas and Flicks and Nitas and Frayas, it could have been quite fun, but LOUISE WAS THERE, so forget it.

Anyway, she got into conversation with Byron and I was apalled to overhear the following exchange:

LOUISE   No, I'm delighted Nigel's done this. I think its so important for him to BECOME INVOLVED IN THE ARTS.

BRYON   Oh yes. Its been super having him. He's been a real treasure. Shy, I would think.

LOUISE   Maybe that's it.

BYRON   Anyway, I'm about to do another production, Cotswold Wanderlust's *Mutual Depression*.

LOUISE   (*clapping her hands with glee*) Oh, how marvellous!

BYRON   And there's a part in it which I think could be Niggles all over. Do you think he might possibly . . .?

LOUISE   Of course he'll do it.

BYRON   Well, if you wouldn't mind asking . . . .

LOUISE   I'll tell him.
               ERRRRRGH.

Actualy I got out of that rather neatly. On the way back in the car I said to Louise, 'Byron is doing another production soon. I hope there's a part for me in it. Fraya's going to be in it. And I do find her very dishy.'

That was the last I heard of me being involved in any more Amatuer Dramatics.

I'VE JUST HAD A GHASTLY THOUGHT . . . .
    SUPPOSE TIMOTHY PEASON READS THIS BOOK
. . . THEN HE'LL FIND OUT ABOUT . . . .
    On second thoughts, it'll be all right.
    HE DOESN'T READ.

10

HOLIDAYS

Or, We Must do the Packing, Mustn't You?

My attitude to holidays has changed. When I think back to the ends of terms at St Cs, the mounting exitement, the delicious prospect of GETTING AWAY from Grimes, prunes, Sigismund the Mad Maths Master, bullies, Basil F-T saying hello clouds hello sky, Latin, Miss Pringle, ink darts, the school dog ect., I wonder in retraspect how my young heart stood the strain.

POETIC BIT:

> Ah the sweet follies of youth, longing only for escape, thinking not of the morrow, delighted only to say adieu to yesterday and luxureate in today! Ah the joy of casting off the shackles of the schoolroom, to be a boy free as the wind gambling careless through the pastures of experience!

END OF POETIC BIT.

Now I am more cynical.

Yes, I am delighted at the prospect of GETTING AWAY from Grint, Invoice Docketting (Internal – and, come to that, External), Darryl Pacey, the other gnomes, GBH House, Celia's debquacking – it's even quite a relief to the blood vessles to get away from the disturbing flashes of Charleen's thigh.

But life is not so black and white as it used to be. *Now* being on holiday brings its own problems. To put it bluntly, it means BEING WITH LOUISE, TRISTRAM AND LUCINDA.

Now of course I love my family dearly (as you will by now have gathered from this book, whose every page drips with martial and paternal affection), but ENOUGH IS ENOUGH. In fact, I find the averige weekend is QUITE ENOUGH.

But everyone needs a holiday, all work and no play makes

Nigel even duller and other apropriate clichés . . . so I just have to grin and bare it.

Louise's approach to planning a holiday is pretty much the same as Atilla the Huns. And its affects are equally devastating (esp. on me).

Before Christmas she starts drawing up her battle-lines, building up supplies of broschures ect. and announcing the economies we are going to have to undertake to make it possible.

This leads pretty soon to comments on our poverty, with implyed criticism of me. Why am I still only on CJ2/B level when other people (yes, we know who) get to that grade much earlier? Wouldnt it be worth going to see Grint to discus promotion?

I respond to this with apropriate hollow laughter, but it is usualy suficcient to spoil Christmas (not, let's face it, a difficult task). Apart from anything else, Christmas gives a fortaste of our summer holiday, demonstrating exactly how well Louise, Tristram, Lucinda, Louise's Mother and I get on when we're together for any length of time.

The awful thing about this proscess of discussion and decision is that THE END IS NEVER IN DOUBT.

However exotic the broschures, whatever calculations we make that by living on bread and water we can afford Greece, WE ALWAYS END UP WITH LOUISE'S MOTHER AT RUSTINGTON-ON-SEA.

There are disadvantages to this, viz.:

1 Louise's mother.
2 The weather.
3 Louise.
4 The children.
5 Rustington-on-Sea.

But let's look on the bright side – there are advantages too, viz.:

1 It's cheap.
2 Free baby-sitting by Louise's Mother if Louise and I want to go out anywhere in the evening.
3 Um . . . .
4 Er . . . .
5 Well, that's about it . . . .

138

So its hey-ho, load up the car with buckets and spades, check wether the moth has got into the swimming togs or not and there's no need to look like that, Nigel, we're going to have a really good holiday.

And its slopping over wet sand, perching uncomfortabley on pebbles, being asked for icecreams every five minutes, being told I ought to be reading something 'with a bit more meat in it than that rubbish you got at the kiosk'. It's a fortnight of being polite to Louise's Mother. (At the end of it one year, I was seriously worried that exessive smiling had given me *rigour mortis* of the facial mussels. I mentioned this to Timothy Peason over a few theraputic pts in the Coach and Hounds and he said I'd always been dead from the neck up anyway. I tell you, the Alquonguin Round Table had nothing on him.)

Its also time to ENTERTAIN THE CHILDREN. Ergh. Since the only things they want to do are go to the funfair or bury me in the sand, this gets very tedious.

Whats more, Louise doesnt help. She settles down under a beach umberella with a copy of *The Best Incomprehensable Finnish Short Stories* (pub. Grabber & Grabber Pretensious Books @ £12.95) and says, 'No, Nigel, I have them all the year round. A holiday is an oportunity for them to GET TO KNOW THEIR FATHER.'

When she says this, Tristram and Lucinda look at me like something that's been brought in for their first Biology Practical and, the expression of loathing still on their faces, ask for another icecream.

And so it goes on every year. Inexerably (good word, huh?). But, you know, sometimes, when the house is full of travel broschures, I fantesize about what my IDEAL HOLIDAY would be . . . .

ATMOS : THE HOTEL ORGIA

Come to the Hotel Orgia for the holiday of a lifetime!

Atmos is the perfect Greek island, a magnet for hosts of beautiful bikini-clad women looking for a man with SOMETHING SPECIAL TO OFFER!

Sunshine and Sucess With Women are Guaranteed All The Year Round!

So what will it be like when you come to the Hotel Orgia?

Your day will start around noon when an attractive chambermaid brings your breakfast and does for you whatever you were dreaming about when you woke up.

Then hotel porters will carry you down to the poolside where you can have a few beers (English, not that continental rubbish) and watch the talent.

Why not have lunch there? Just snap your fingers for service and you'll get it. All our waiters speak English. They will serve you quickly and defferentialy and will not try to ace you out with the girls round the pool (or at the disco later on). They are specialy selected for their ugliness.

And what about the food at the Hotel Orgia? You'll certainley enjoy it! None of that foriegn rubbish – but take your pick of sausages, stakes, liver and bacon, fried eggs, chips, jam rollypolly, tomatoe kechup ect., ect.

You'll also find the local wine is cheap and easy, as are the local women.

After you've had some of that, forklift trucks will remove you, on your airbed, from the poolside to the Nude Bathing Beach Observation Platform, where you will be provided with unlimited bottles of chilled white wine and a pair of binoculers.

(The care we take in the selection of our clientelle insures that no one on the beach will have bigger mussels or be browner than you are. Nor is there any of that watersking, windserfing, vollyball nonsense ect., that might make you look silly.)

Maybe, after an hour or so of that, you'll fancy a *Siesta*? Or why not try the suana or jackuzi, where jetsetting lovlies will vye for your favours. Anyway, have a rest to get ready for the famous NIGHT-LIFE, which is what gives the hotel its name!

(For those of you afflicted with Children there is a 24-hour *cresche*. There is also a similar service provided for Wives, so that men can enjoy the exottic NIGHT-LIFE without anxiety.)

So your on your own and can enjoy everything that cheap booze, soft lights and avid ladies can offer!

And when finally you fall into bed in the small hours at the Hotel Orgia, YOU'LL FEEL A DIFFRENT PERSON (due to a rather clever lottery we've worked out with the bedroom keys).

Yes, come to the Hotel Orgia – for the holiday designed for YOU!

(The hotel reserves the right to refuse bookings from unsuitable aplicants (e g. Grint, Darrylandcarryl, the F-Ts ect.); and there is a hotel rule that anyone who mentions GBH will be summarily ejected.

There is also a quaint local custom that people whose intials are N.M. dont have to pay for anything.)

But it'll never happen. I know it. Back to Rustington-on-Sea, dodging the showers, stepping over the fossils on the beach (and in the supermarket).

It is a wellknown psycological fact that NO ONE IS EVEN MILDLY INTERESTED IN ANYONE ELSE'S HOL- IDAY, but, in spite of this, people still insist on sending post- cards. You know the sort of thing I mean . . . .

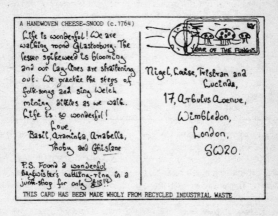

A HANDWOVEN CHEESE-SNOOD (c.1764)

Life is wonderful! We are walking round Glastonbury. The lesser spikeweed is blooming and our Cay-Anes are straitening out. We practise the steps of folk-songs and sing Welch mining ditties as we walk. Life is so wonderful!

Love,
Basil, Araminta, Anabella, Thoby and Ghislane

P.S. Found a wonderful Barfwister's cuddling-rena in a junk-shop for only £18!!

Nigel, Louise, Tristram and Lucinda,
17, Arbulus Avenue,
Wimbledon,
London,
SW20.

THIS CARD HAS BEEN MADE WHOLY FROM RECYCLED INDUSTRIAL WASTE

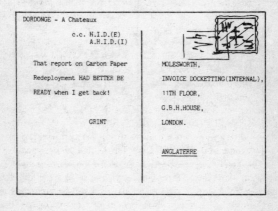

DORDONGE - A Chateaux

c.c. H.I.D.(E)
A.H.I.D.(I)

That report on Carbon Paper Redeployment HAD BETTER BE READY when I get back!

GRINT

MOLESWORTH,
INVOICE DOCKETTING(INTERNAL),
11TH FLOOR,
G.B.H.HOUSE,
LONDON.

ANGLATERRE

LANZAROTTI - Sunshine Beach
LANZAROTTI - Bicha del Sol
LANZAROTTI - Vonsonnonsbitsch

Pissed again
last night.
Sharon's got a
new bikini on
- just!
    The Pearsons

The Ploesworth
    family
17, Arbutus Ave
WIMBLEDON

INGLITTERA

MAJORCA - Nude Beach
MAJORCA - Bicha del Bubios
MAJORCA - Titzenbumsenbitsch

It is really
nice here. I
am having a
really nice
time.
    Charleen

All on the 11th
    Floor,
G.B.H. House,
    London,
Inglhittierra

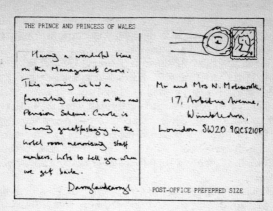

THE PRINCE AND PRINCESS OF WALES

Having a wonderful time
on the Management Course.
This morning we had a
fascinating lecture on the new
Pension Scheme. Carole is
having great fun staying in the
hotel room memorising staff
numbers. Lots to tell you when
we get back.

Danny Carole and Carol

Mr and Mrs N. Molesworth,
17, Arbutus Avenue,
Wimbledon,
London SW20 9QC5210B

POST-OFFICE PREFERRED SIZE

FUN IN A MASSAGE PARLOR!

GETTING
REALY LAIDBACK
AND LAID!
WOW!

STEVE

MOLESWORTHS,
WIMBLEDON,
ANGELUND

Actualy, when I said Louise and I ALWAYS end up at
Rustington, that is a slight exageration. We have had holidays
abroad, but not for years. Not really since we've had the
children.

This is quite a relief in many ways. You've already gathered
from the description of the Hotel Orgia (q.c.) what my ideal
foriegn holiday is. LOUISE'S IS NOT EXACTLY THE
SAME.

In fact, it's totally diffrent. Her idea of bliss is to find some-where which is surounded by Art and Culture and spend a fortnight doing daytrips to museums, monuments, ruins, gal-leries ect. I find all that a bit waring.

We had a holiday like that in Tuscany just before we had Tristram. (In fact I think it was then that Louise decided we would have Tristram.) I hated it. My view is that when you see one painting you can imagine pretty well what the others are going to be like, but Louise insists on seeing everything.

A few days ago I came across the broschure for the town we stayed in. It brought every detail of the holiday back. (I had to nip down the Coach and Hounds for a couple of pts with Peason to recover.)

All those broschures are the same really. Written by people who cant speak English. And the spelling – dear oh dear, it is ABSOLUTELY APALLING!

You know the sort of thing . . . .

SAN GARBAGIO

Here is center for touristic panoramic and gasterognomic artistic pleasures! This cramped town-in-wall, mislaid in folded hills like jewell in purse, is dripping with histories!

Here in Century Fourteen Turkish worriers try to turn people to infidelity but pigheaded local spirit did not allow. Two century later popal wars caused much spasms, but inmates not upended. Same bloodyminded character still today!

Coinciding meanwhile, artistic side flowers. San Garbagio home-town of Luigi Della Posco, whose great pincture is still a vision on alter fresko in Church of the Blessed Enunciation. His great doings now in pockets of collectors over world.

As well arcitectural! Many wizzened buildings are going back to Century Fifteen with peculier bevelled gables of area distinktive. Small tortured roots neccesary arteries lead blood of town to grandiose square, Piaza Della Posco, where old men gather in evening to do old men activities. Anything goes in San Garbagio – as tourist soon unearths!

And for fodder – what a variation in quality! Fish come here specialy from all locality and tournished with sources that are unearthly! Good stuffing a feauture of all restarants native! Nature's excess in fruity form also all over you!

And for wine! Local vinyards stream down crushed into bottles. The sangiune Parosco slips like catteract, refreshing mostly! And candid Barusco masturbates the tongue! Oh pleasurable tittilation!

For all traveler San Garbagio is an order. Whatever your proclivaties, here you will find your heart's end!

San Garbagio – a jewell whose flavour will linger on the interior of your brain for all!

One terrible thing about holidays is that EVERYONE TAKES PHOTOGRAPHS. O.K., you may say, that's a harmless enough activitty – what people do in their own time is their own concern. But it's not as simple as that, because people who take photographs do not just do it for their own bennefit. THEY EXPECT OTHER PEOPLE TO LOOK AT THEM.

Oh dear, oh dear, the tedium on the 11th Floor at GBH House a week after someone has come back from their hols and they've just had their pictures developped!

There is a rule about holiday snaps and that is: WHATEVER THERE IS AROUND, NO ONE EVER PHOTOGRAPHS ANYTHING INTERESTING.

I mean take Charleen. After you know she's spent a fortnight sunbathing on a nude beach, you might be forgiven for awaiting her holiday pictures with a degree of interest. But you'd be wrong. *'That's the sea . . . and that bit's a sort of headland . . . and that was a tree we saw . . . and this is the hotel . . . there's one of the entrance to the disco . . . .'* ect., ect., ect. Very disapointing.

I came to the conclusion a few years back that the only way to counter this mennace was by showing my own holiday snaps. Goodness, a few shots of Rustington-on-Sea should be suficcient to make the point. No one would trouble me with their little efforts after that.

But it doesnt seem to have worked. In fact I think it's made things worse. I get shown more holiday snaps than ever. Perhaps my having shown mine gets them going on the well-known kindagarden principal ('I'll show you mine if you'll show me yours'). Or maybe they're just getting their revenge for all those views of Rustington-on-Sea.

11

SEX

Or, Now Let's Be Grown-Up About This, Snigger, Snigger

There is no question about it – attitudes to sex have changed since I was young.

When I think back to the illinformed sniggerings at St Cs and the more detailed (but equally illinformed) after-lights-out conversations in the dorms at Grunts, and compare it to the amazing display of information and visual aids available to the modern addlescent, I realise just how much has changed.

Wheras we used to pass around a copy of *Her Burning Flame* (pub. Grabber & Grabber @ 5/6d) just for pages 47, 173 and 242, or go up to London on half-holidays to see scratchy films of nudists hiding behind beachballs, the young person of today can go into any sex-shop and buy hard-core books (so I'm told), put 50p in a slot-machine and see videos of people actualy you know (again so I have been told) or go to cinema-clubs and see films like this one about the bloke who goes round to dinner with these two girls who wait till they get to the pudding and then take all his clothes off and put chocolate moose all over his . . . well, that sort of thing, which is the kind of thing that can now be seen (though of course I only report what I have been told. I don't want you to get the impression that I'm the sort of person who goes to that sort of show, not the sort of person who is a member of the Naughtirama Club in Frith Street Programmes Change Every Week Only Five Pounds Membership. No thats not my sort of scene at all.)

Not only are these sources of information available, the schools also take part, so that every child in the country knows EVERYTHING by the time its twelve.

This is meant to make for a MUCH HEALTHIER ATTI-

TUDE TO SEX. No longer need it be something furtive. There is now no shame attatched. Nothing to snigger about.

THIS IS THOUGHT TO BE A GREAT IM-PROVEMENT.

I'm not so sure . . . .

You see, the way I see it, the furtiveness and the shame and the sniggerring were PART OF THE FUN. If you cease to think of sex as A BIT NAUGHTY, then where's the attraction?

'But low!' the forces of libberation cry. 'At last – we have acheived guilt-free sex!'

To me this has the same appeal as alcohol-free lager. What's the point of doing it, I ask, if you dont feel guilty and have a good snigger afterwards?

Now it'd be diffrent if the GUILT itself had gone.

But it hasn't.

It's just been shifted to other things.

Much simpler in the days when it was just Sex and Blasphemy . . . .

(Ye scene is ye village greene in ye darke ages. Two yolkels are looking at an unrepentent figure in ye stocks.)

1ST YOLKEL	Byre Laykin and Ods Gillygaskins! Ist not Goodman Molesworth here in durence vile?
2ND YOLKEL	Cods eggs and little chippings! But tis he!
1ST YOLKEL	What hath he done to earn this cruel fete?
2ND YOLKEL	Ah, he were taken in Goodwoman Charleen's cottage, in ye acte of prooving that she were notte as goode a woman as she's mayde oute to bee.
1ST YOLKEL	Caught without his breaches, by St Micheal! Adulterie!
2ND YOLKEL	Aye, by St Ockings! Butte twas on ye Sabbathe to boote!
1ST YOLKEL	Bootynge on ye Sabbathe, by St Ruth! Tis Blasphamy!

2ND YOLKEL	Aye! Let us throw all these rotten apples, egges, olde cornflake packettes, bittes of orange peele, beercannes, ecte. at himme!
2ND YOLKEL	Aye, readylye! *(They do so.)*

O.K. Primitive I grant you.

But at least YOU KNEW WHERE YOU STOOD.

Wheras now you have just as much guilt, but not about things its worth feeling guilty about.

YOU ARE MADE TO FEEL GUILTY BY:

1 The Dental Hygenist, for not using your Floss.
2 The Fotherington-Thomases, for not reusing envelops.
3 Darrylandcarryl, for not *actualy caring* about the GBH Revised Pension Sceme Proposals.
4 My apalling brother Steve, for not spending all your time having hundreds of loose women and smoking ilegal substances.
5 Louise, for almost everything.

BRINGE BACKE YE DARKE AGES, as far as I'm concerned.

Peoples sex lives of course are BIG SECRETS and there is no rational explaination for most sexual attraction. I mean, some is obvious (like why Peason fancies Sharon), but some is totally bazaar (like why Sharon fancies Peason).

People look for different things in a marriage (except for Darryl Pacey who must have been looking for himself when he met Carole). Basil F-T was looking for Arrabella when he met Araminta. Grabber was looking for a GOOD INVESTMENT when he selected Felicitiah. And I, when I met Louise, was looking for . . . hem-hem, well we neednt go into that.

What I'm really getting at is that in sexual matters – take it from one who knows – apearances are deceptive. Bespectackled little mice turn out to be real ravers, and apparent sexpots can be revealed by an inapropriate hand on a random thigh to have taken various unattractive religious vows at a very early age.

Charleen at the office is a good example of what I mean.

Charleen at the office is AMAZING. Yes I know she looks

amazing and has all of Invoice Docketting (Internal) (and presumabley most of the Rest of the World [External]) lusting after her, but the amazing thing I was going to comment on is not that. It is the fact that she reads ROMANTIC FICTION.

You'd have thought someone like her was getting enough of the REAL THING not to have need of such FANTESY SURREGATES.

But no. Every day beside her typewriter is the latest in the Mills & Grabber 'Heartbeat' series, so obviously that is what TURNS HER ON.

So her vacuous expression is not, as we had all assumed, due to sexual satiety (not a bad phrase, huh?); it is because she is dreaming of MR RIGHT suddenly walking into her life.

Sometimes I try to gatecrash that dream . . . .

LOVE AND PATIENTS

by Madeleine Eglantine

Chapter One

Nurse Charleen Rose tried to focuss her eyes on the temperature charts at the foot of the bed, but they blurred over with unwanted tears. The memory of the night before still spread like a blush through her being.

She had felt so sure of Brent Masterly. Oh, they had never spoken of the future, never mentioned marriage, it hadnt seemed important, they had all the time in the world . . . . But she had thought they had had an understanding. Wrong. A misunderstanding more likely, she reflected bitterly.

She could still hear his voice – not the soft voice of their moonlight walks and the windserfing on that timeless holiday in Creet, but a new harsh voice, the voice of ambition, a voice that excluded tenderness and love.

'I've accepted a job deepseadiving in Saudi Arabia, Charleen. I start tomorrow.'

What a bombshell that had been! Even as she remembered his words, she knew Brent's plane would be winging over Europe to his new destiney, his new wealth and, who could say, probably a new love.

And she was left washed up on the beach, the flotsome of the spring tide of his ambition.

'Concentrate, Nurse Rose. This patient is meant to have 10 c.c. of Lythamythagobinol, not 100 c.c.'

The harsh voice brought her back to reality. Were all the voices in her life to be harsh now that Brent was gone forever?

'I'm sorry, Doctor.'

'Another late night was it, Nurse?'

'Well yes, I . . . .'

His gaze engaged with hers. For a moment there seemed a soffening in the Doctor's customery harshness, a fleck of sympathy in those steel-grey eyes.

But it vanished. She must have imagined it.

'No excuses, Nurse. Remember, your primary duty is to your patients. If you join the medical profession, their lives come first, your private life second.'

'Yes, Doctor.'

He turned his ramrod back on her and with his supple heeling fingers probed the patient's scab.

And for the first time Charleen felt some sympathy with his coldness, with that selfless dedication which had made him cut out from his life all emotion with the same precision he demonstrated removing a maline growth in the operating theatre.

But was it just professional dedication or were the stories that went round the Nurses Home true, stories of his having been married once, of a young wife who drowned in a scoober-diving accident on their honeymoon in Accapulco?

Whatever the truth, Charleen decided that she too would build up a defense against the tumultuous world of emotion, a hard shell against the soft blandishments of love. She would harden her heart and live for her work, like Dr Molesworth.

'Help! There's an emergency!'

The Doctor turned his ramrod back and fixed his steel-grey eyes on the person who had just burst in through the door . . . .

BUT NO. My fantesy is shattered again. It is not a young houseman telling me that only my supple heeling fingers can save the life of a Member of The Royal Family in Intentsive Care; it is GRINT asking me why the hell I havent finished my report on Paperclip Recquisitioning Proceedure.

And my campain to show Charleen that I am really MR RIGHT and how about a quick cuddle behind the coffee-machine is set back once again . . . .

Actualy you know, it's worth remembering that all women are suckers for ROMANCE. Even in this neon-and-vynil-age (not bad, huh?), the ROMANTIC APPROACH may prove to be more sucessful than the brutally physical.

NB – It is always a good wheeze to let a woman think you WRITE POETRY. Not only will she then think that you have GREAT DEPTH OF SENSABILITY; she will also put down any wrything and moaning you do in her presence to CREATIVE ANGIUSH and not just LUST.

And if you can pretend that you write poetry ABOUT HER, you will really get her going. (Poets always do well with women, it's a well-known fact. To have a poem written about her is one of the great desires of all women – with the possible exception of Eskimo Nell.)

The trouble is that actualy writing poetry is PURGETORY and doing it more than once is SHERE MASHOCISM. So the best thing to do is to write one that is adjustible, so that it'll do for anyone.

Here is a modest example of my own (which only took me about 3 and a ½ years to complete) . . . .

TO MY BELOVED

A Sonnit by Nigel Molesworth

[Delete where inaplicable]

Ah Love, what Breeze does yonder Zepher blow
That Stirs the leaves about my manley trunk?
'Tis Dum-Dum's* voice that makes me tremble so,
Her sweet | blue   eyes that make me feel so drunk.
        | brown
        | black
        | green
        | grey

Fine feathers shimmer on the | fairest   birds –
                            | brownest
                            | blackest
                            | reddest
                            | whitest

* This is not meant for anyone actualy called Dum-Dum – that's just for rythm. WHATEVER YOU DO DONT FALL FOR ANYONE WITH MORE THAN 2 SILLABLES – Ed.

My Dum-Dum's hair I know is { fairer   still,
                              browner
                              blacker
                              redder
                              whiter

Nor makes their song such music as her words
Of which my thirsty ears ne'er drink their fill.
And oh! her statuer is still my delight!
Ne'er came perfection in a form so { small!
                                     tall!

And dreams of her iradiate my night
And in the morn { these lines to her I scrawl.†
                  into her arms I fall.

{ Beleive my love, and meet my love so true
  With your own love, your heart – and body too!‡
  In the King's Arms, where we can have a few!
  And may your husband never have a clue!
  When my Louise has gone to stay in Crewe!
  Behind the coffee-machine at half-past-two!

WIFESWOPPING. No one has ever asked me to swop my
wife.

The moment has never come when, 'Well, it was late, we'd
had a few drinks and somehow the conversation got round to
sex; before we knew it we . . . .' As I say it's never happened.

I PUT THIS DOWN TO BEING MARRIED TO
LOUISE.

But I know it is suposed to go on. There are Dark Rumours
of such things happenning even in the leafy purleius of Wimbledon (not to mention such more obvious centres of deparavity
as Orpington, Blackheath, Twickenam and Totteridge).

What strikes me about it is that it must be very difficult to
get a FAIR SWOP. Certainley that's true if my experiense with
conkers back at St Cs is anything to go by. Someone like
Grabber always got the big round beauties, wheras I ended up
with the little wizzened cracked ones.

I'M SURE IT MUST BE THE SAME WITH WIVES.

† Depending on how the relationship's going – Ed.
‡ Depending on who the relationship's with – Ed.

And well, when its late, you've had a few drinks and somehow the conversation has got round to sex, it may not be the moment to start argueing about wether your getting a fair deal or not.

Perhaps it would help if their was a Grading System for Wives. (I'm sure Darrylandcarryl could work out something.) It needn't be very complicated – just a form the husband fills in at the beginning of the sort of evening when its likely to, well, get late, your likely to have a few drinks and somehow the conversation's likely to get round to sex .... Points would be awarded for SEXINESS, CHARM, SENSE OF HUMOUR, SEXINESS, SILENCE AT APROPRIATE MOMENTS, ect. Then the totals could be asessed and FAIR SWOPS worked out.* And if there were any serious imballances, then you'd be allowed to make up the weight in *au pere* girls.

The only disadvantage of this system is a big one: HOW WOULD I EVER AMMASS ENOUGH POINTS FOR LOUISE TO MAKE HER A FAIR SWOP FOR SHARON PEASON?

SEXUAL PROBLEMS. Sex is all out in the opon these days (If you dont beleive me, try walking over Wimbledon Common on a summer evening.)

The great new libberated principal is : EVERYTHING (AND PARTICULARLEY SEX) IS BETTER IF YOU TALK ABOUT IT.

This has led to a lot of FRANK AND FORTHRIGHT† television programmes and radio phone-ins dealing exclusively with SEXUAL PROBLEMS. There are also many EXTREMELY SERIOUS, NO-NONSENSE‡ magazines on the subj., bought by tired buisnessmen on stn. bookstalls to give them a breif intelude of fantesy between the devisive realities of Office and Home (more classy stuff).

These magazines are full of letters written by anxious members of the public (or bored members of the editorial staff) about their sexlifes, followed by serious comments and advice

---

* This might at last be SOMETHING USEFUL that could be done by those Home Computers they keep advertising – Ed.

† i.e. Dirty – Ed.

‡ Dirty again – Ed.

by A DOCTOR.* The aim of all the letters is TO GIVE THE READER A GOOD SNIGGER.

Things like this . . . .

SHEER BLISS ♀

I just had to write on this lovely day to say how happy my marrage is. I have the most wonderful husband in the world, two marvelous children, a very dear sister-in-law, the varigated knapwert is blooming and everything is super.

A. F-T, Wimbledon.

A DOCTOR COMMENTS : *This is abnormal.*

SOME STUD ♂

I made love to 7493 different women last year. This is certainley a Personal Best and I beleive it may be an All-Comers Record. Could you confirm this for me?

S. M., Notting Hill

A DOCTOR COMMENTS : *Shut up! I dont beleive you (well I do actualy which makes it worse – FUMES OF JEALOUSY).*

GLEESOME THREESOME ♀

My husband is a wonderful man who is very dedicated to his work. Our sexlife is wonderful, but I sometimes wonder if am doing enough for his pleasure. I know he is a great admiror of his wondeful boss at work and I wonder whether I should suggest the boss joins us for a session in bed one night. I think it might help my husband get to the point of CJ2/A quicker. What is your advice?

C. P., Tooting

A DOCTOR COMMENTS : *There are very few things that can be done between a man and a woman that are truely disgusting, but what you suggest is one of them. You filthy little sycaphant!*

* For reasons of professional ethics, the Doctor has to remain anonnymous, but he is of course Dr. N. Molesworth, F.R.C.P., F.R.C.S., S.N.C.F., T.G.W.U. – Ed.

SEXY DRESSER ♂

My wife always wears very tight sweaters and skirts and other garments that reveal her contours to the whole world. Is this all right?

T. P., Wandsworth

A DOCTOR COMMENTS : *Its all right by ME.*

WILLING SERVANTS ♀

I have recently heard from The Little Woman Who Has Sex For Me that The Little Man Who Has Sex For My Husband has been having an affair with The Little Woman Who Has Affairs For Me. Should I mention that I know to The Little Man Who Talks To My Husband For Me or just ignore it?

F. G., The Rt. Hon., Knightsbridge, St Mortiz, St Lucia, St Troppez, ect.

A DOCTOR COMMENTS : *This kind of thing is commoner than you might think. My advise to you is to get back into your bank valt and forget about it.*

TO GROPE OR NOT TO GROPE ♂

There's this girl at the office I really fancy. Her name's Charleen and she shows no sigh of fancying me but I wonder if that's just because her sexualitty is latant. I think the matter could be decided if I were to try a quick grope behind the coffee-machine. Or would that be too riskey? And how likely is my wife to find out?

N. M., Wimbledon

A DOCTOR COMMENTS : *Oops!*

The other fassinating parts of these INSTRUCTIVE AND THERAPUTIC magazines are the small adds . . . .

PERSONAL CLASSIFIEDS

SEXY Libran seeks ditto Acquarian. Object Librarians. BOX 2278

FLY THE FLADGE! Former Headmaster Eddie "Anything For A Quid" Grimes offers corective dissipline. BOX 391

MARTIAL AIDS. A wide selection available at our showrooms. GRABBOPORN, Crewe

ESSEX threesome seeks local foursome with a view to vulgar fractions. BOX 542

PASSIVE MALE seeks passive female with view to nice quiet evenings over cocoa. BOX 3247

VIDEOS — Jayne Mansfield Park, Winnie the Poof, Orgasm Gaiters, Sex Characters in Search of the Other, many other titles. BOX 211

WANT AN ESCORT FOR THAT 'SPECIAL' EVENING? You'll not be disappointed at Grimes Used Car Sales, Dagenam.

RUBBER PEOPLE — Meet others with similar interests at Wimbledon Bridge Club.

MEN IT CAN BE DONE! Let Winkler's Unique Formula Smacopac get you to CJ2/A level quicker and keep you there longer than ever before!

THE MOLESWORTH DO-IT-YOURSELF SOFT-PORN-WRITER (Pats. Pending)

(Simpley choose any combination of 5 numbers between 1 + 20 for the erotic experiense of a lifetime.)

HE/SHE	HER/HIS		WITH A	
1 throbbed	1 throbbing	1 secret	1 throbbing	1 throb.
2 pulsated	2 pulsating	2 part	2 pulsating	2 pulsation.
3 urged	3 urgent	3 nub	3 nurgent	3 urgensy.
4 stimulated	4 magnificent	4 chihwahwa*	4 blind	4 finger.
5 tickled	5 soft	5 core	5 probing	5 hand.
6 stroked	6 velvetty	6 flesh	6 burning	6 foot.
7 touched	7 silken	7 area	7 firey	7 circular motion.
8 beat	8 moist	8 treasure	8 flaming	8 passion.
9 probed	9 secret	9 thing	9 nacellerating	9 vibration.
10 triggered	10 responsive	10 flame	10 nelectric	10 sigh.
11 twiddled	11 melting	11 whatnot	11 nunending	11 ryhthm.
12 squeezed	12 intruiging	12 sanctum	12 noxy-acetylyn*	12 fire.
13 vibrated	13 yeilding	13 masculinitty	13 greedy	13 touch.
14 surendered to	14 double-glazed*	14 femininity	14 throbbing	14 massage.
15 siezed	15 burning	15 response	15 compelling	15 feeling.
16 grasped	16 sensual	16 thigh	16 silkey	16 little cry.
17 fingerred	17 proud	17 mystery	17 hightening	17 ecstacy.
18 photocopied*	18 throbbing	18 centre	18 wild	18 bundle of birch twigs
19 rubbed	19 rubberised	19 splendor	19 damp	19 toothbrush*.
20 exited	20 willing	20 triangle	20 nintimite	20 sensuality.

* Catering for specialist tastes – Ed.

12

ENVOIE

I've often seen that word at the end of pretensious books Louise leaves lying around, so I supose it must be Pretensious for THE END.

So, anyway, wishing this book to apeal to a slightly classier mkt. than it might otherwise, I'm putting ENVOIE at the end.

Well, what can I say . . .?

As the afternoon of my life melts impeceptibly into evening (How *about* that?), as experiense profers its hairbrush to my receeding hairline, as the supple limbs of youth freeze into arthritis, as the gushing arterries of inspiration dry into the dusty riverbeds of immitation (This is getting better by the minute – perhaps I should go back, start again and do the whole book in this style – might apeal to a *nicer* class of person), I am glad to have shared a few of my thoughts with you. Who knows, perhaps something I have written has stirred a cord in your nostaglic heart.

Oh, if it has, know what joy I feel to realise that the vibrations within my cerrebellum have found an answerring ryhthm in your own.

And if it hasn't, well . . . SEE IF I CARE.

PHEW!

Hard work that was.

Right, quick look round.

Tristram and Lucinda are playing Mass Murderers upstairs.

Louise is ingrossed in a prog. on the telly about the social and religious pressures against the cooking of wholefood in Paragauy.

Fine.

I'm going to nip down to the Coach and Hounds for a few pts with Peason.